GCSE DESIGN AND TECHNOLOG

Food Technology

Belinda Campbell
Barbara Clapton
Catherine Tipton

Edexcel
Success through qualifications

Heinemann Educational Publishers
Halley Court, Jordan Hill, Oxford, OX2 8EJ
a division of Reed Educational & Professional Publishing Ltd

OXFORD MELBOURNE AUCKLAND
JOHANNESBURG BLANTYRE GABORONE
IBADAN PORTSMOUTH NH(USA) CHICAGO

First published in 2002

06 05 04 03 02
9 8 7 6 5 4 3 2

British Library Cataloguing in Publication Data
A catalogue record for this book is available from the British Library

ISBN 0 435 417894

Designed and typeset by Hardlines Ltd, Charlbury, Oxford
Picture research by Thelma Gilbert
Printed and bound in Spain by Mateu Cromo

Acknowledgements
The authors and publishers would like to thank the following for permission to use photographs: Alvery Berkel on pp. 50, 51; Anthony Blake Photo Library/Gerrit Buntrock on p. 15; Anthony Blake Photo Library/Maximilian Stock on p. 45; Gareth Boden on pp. 21, 38, 87; Trevor Clifford on p. 7; Elona on pp. 70, 84; Food Features on pp. 19, 21, 36, 41, 71; Linda Haisley, 'Cakes for all Occasions', 7 Newland Mill, Witney, Oxon, OX8 6HH, 01993 705990 on pp. 59, 64; Holt Studios/Richard Anthony on p. 81; Holt Studios/Nigel Cattlin on p. 93; Chris Honeywell/Hayden Bakery on pp. 34, 54; KPT Power Photos on p. 35; National Dairy Council on p. 68; Network/Barry Lewis on p. 97; Panasonic Home Appliance Marketing on pp. 60, 61; Philip Parkhouse on p. 38; Photodisc on pp. 15, 23; Steve Richardson on pp. 64, 67; Roger Scruton on pp. 6, 8, 9, 13, 18, 20, 22, 24, 28, 32, 39, 40, 42, 43, 49, 51, 56, 61, 63, 66, 68, 69, 72, 73, 76, 77, 90, 95; Trip/H. Rogers on p. 87; Warburtons on pp. 74, 75. Thanks is also given to Northern Foods.

The publishers have made every effort to trace the copyright holders, but if they have inadvertently overlooked any, they will be pleased to make the necessary arrangements at the first opportunity.

Cover photographs by: John Birdsall, Gareth Boden and Noon Products.

Tel: 01865 888058 www.heinemann.co.uk

Contents

Introduction

Welcome to this GCSE student book, which has been specially written to support you as you work through your Design and Technology course. If you are following a short-course, check with your teacher to see which sections of the book you need to cover. You can find out information about the full-course and the short-course in the next couple of pages.

How to use this book

This student book will help you develop knowledge and understanding about the specialist materials area you have chosen to study within Design and Technology. It includes sections on:

- the classification and selection of materials
- preparing, processing and finishing materials
- manufacturing commercial products
- design and market influence.

As you work through each section, you will find 'Things to do', which test your understanding of what you have learned. Your teacher may ask you to undertake these tasks in class or for homework.

At the end of each section you will find a number of questions that are similar in style to the ones in the end-of-course exam. In preparation for your exam it is a good idea to put down on a single side of A4 paper all the key points about a topic. Use sub-headings or bullet point lists and diagrams to help you organize what you know. If you do this regularly throughout the course, you will find it easier to revise for the exam.

The book also includes sections that cover the coursework requirements of the full-course and the short-course. These coursework sections will guide you through all the important designing and making stages of your coursework. They explain:

- how to organize your project
- what you have to include
- how the project is marked
- what you have to do to get the best marks.

You should refer to the coursework sections as and when you need.

The GCSE Design and Technology full-course

The GCSE Design and Technology full-course builds on the experience you had of all the five materials areas at Key Stage 3:

- Food Technology
- Textiles Technology
- Resistant Materials Technology
- Graphic Products
- Systems and Control Technology.

Each of the five materials areas will provide opportunities for you to demonstrate your design and technology capability. You should therefore specialize in a materials area that best suits your particular skills and attributes.

What will I study?

Throughout the full-course you will have the opportunity to study:

- materials and **components**
- production processes
- industrial processes
- social, moral, ethical and environmental issues of products design
- product analysis
- designing and making processes.

The content of this student book will provide you with all the knowledge and understanding you need to cover during the full-course.

You will then apply this knowledge and understanding when designing and making a 3D product and when producing an A3 folder of design work. You should spend up to 40 hours on your coursework project, which accounts for 60 per cent of your Design and Technology course.

At the end of the full course you will be examined on your knowledge and understanding of your chosen materials area. There will be a $1\frac{1}{2}$ hour exam, worth 40 per cent of the total marks. The exam will be made up of four questions, each worth 10 per cent of the marks.

The GCSE Design and Technology short-course

The GCSE Design and Technology short-course is equivalent to half a full GCSE and will probably be delivered in half the time of the full-course. It involves the study of HALF the content of the full GCSE, and the development of HALF the amount of coursework.

The GCSE short-course allows you to work in the materials area you feel best suits your own particular skills and attributes. You can choose from:

- Food Technology
- Textiles Technology
- Resistant Materials Technology
- Graphic Products
- Systems and Control Technology.

The content of this student book will provide you with all the knowledge and understanding you need to cover during the short-course.

You will then apply this knowledge and understanding when designing and making a 3D product and when producing an A3 folder of design work. You should spend up to 20 hours on your coursework project, which accounts for 60 per cent of your Design and Technology course.

At the end of the short-course you will be examined on your knowledge and understanding of your chosen materials area. There will be a 1-hour exam, worth 40 per cent of the total marks. The exam will be made up of three questions.

Managing your own learning during the course

At GCSE level you are expected to take *some* responsibility for planning your own work and managing your own learning. The ability to do this is an essential skill at Advanced Subsidiary (AS) and Advanced GCE level. It is also highly valued by employers.

In order that you start to take some responsibility for planning your own work, you need to be very clear about what is expected of you during the course. This book aims to provide you with such information. Helpful hints include:

- Read through the whole of the introduction before you start the course so you fully understand the requirements of either the full-course or the short-course.
- Investigate the coursework sections that give you a 'flavour' of what you are expected to do.
- Check out how many marks are awarded for each of the assessment criteria. The more marks that are available, the more work you will need to achieve them.
- Discuss the coursework deadlines with your teacher so you know how much time is available for your coursework.

ICT skills

There will be opportunities during the course for you to develop your ICT capability through the use of CAD/CAM. You may have the opportunity to use:

- ICT for research and communications, such as using the Internet, E-mail, video conferencing, digital cameras and scanners
- word-processing, databases or spreadsheets for planning, recording, handling and analyzing information
- CAD software to model, prototype, test and modify your design proposals
- CAM using computer controlled equipment.

Understanding industrial and commercial practice

During your GCSE course you will have the opportunity to develop an understanding of the design and manufacture of commercial products by undertaking product analysis.

You should demonstrate your understanding of industrial practices in your designing and making activities, which could include:

- developing design briefs and specifications
- using market research
- modelling and prototyping prior to manufacture
- producing a working schedule that shows how the product is manufactured
- making a high quality product that matches the design proposal
- testing and evaluating your product against the specification to provide feedback on its performance and fitness-for-purpose.

You should also use the appropriate technical words to describe your work. Many of these words are to be found in this book. When the words first appear they are in **bold**. This means that you can look up their meaning in the glossary that appears at the end of the book.

Section A:

The classification and selection of material and components

Nutritional needs

Aims

- To understand the importance of energy and **nutrients** in a healthy diet.
- To consider the government's guidelines for a healthy diet.
- To understand that individuals have different dietary needs.

What are nutrients?

Nutrients are substances found in the foods that we eat. The main nutrients are shown in the diagram below.

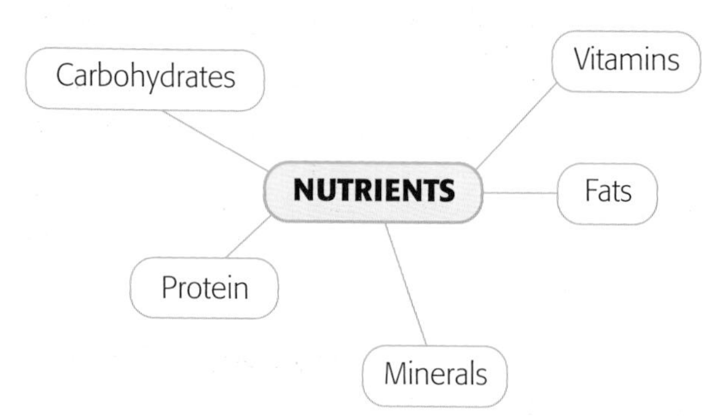

We need a balance of energy and nutrients in our diet to keep us healthy. If there is a deficiency (lack) of energy or a specific nutrient, a health problem may develop. For example, a lack of **iron** in the diet could lead to a condition known as **anaemia**. The importance of each nutrient in the diet will be explored on pages 10-11.

Healthy eating

Eating a good balance and variety of foods is important for a healthy lifestyle. Healthy eating is also about eating in moderation and having regular mealtimes.

A balanced diet

A nutritionally balanced diet will contain the right amount of energy and nutrients to meet the needs of the body. Current healthy eating guidelines also recommend that people eat less sugar, salt and fat, as too much of these could lead to health problems, such as obesity (being very overweight) or heart disease.

Government guidelines

The Balance of Good Health was published in 1994. It was based on eight government guidelines for a healthy diet. It shows the proportion of different types of food you should eat to maintain a balanced, healthy diet.

The eight guidelines are:

1 Enjoy your food.
2 Eat a variety of different foods.
3 Eat the right amount to be a healthy weight.
4 Eat plenty of foods rich in starch and **fibre**.
5 Do not eat too much fat.
6 Do not eat sugary foods too often.
7 Look after the vitamins and minerals in your food.
8 If you drink alcohol, keep within sensible limits.

The government is concerned to see improved health for everyone and promotes *The Balance of Good Health* through the Food Standards Agency (FSA) and the Department of Health. In July 1999, the government published a white paper called *Saving Lives: Our Healthier Nation*. This is an action plan to tackle the problem of poor health in England, with four national targets to reduce deaths from:

- cancer
- heart disease, stroke and related illnesses
- accidents
- mental health related deaths, such as suicide and undetermined injury.

The aim is to see real improvement by the year 2010 and the paper includes recommendations about how individuals could become healthier by:

- increasing intake of fruit, vegetables and fibre
- avoiding high intakes of red and processed meat
- keeping physically active
- maintaining a healthy body weight that does not increase during adult life.

Recommended intake of nutrients

In 1991 the Committee on Medical Aspects of Food Policy (COMA) produced a report detailing **Dietary Reference Values (DRVs)**.

DRVs are the daily nutritional requirements for groups of people of different ages and gender who are in good health. For most nutrients the values are **Reference Nutrient Intake (RNI)**. This is how much of the nutrient needs to be taken to meet the nutritional needs of almost everyone (around 97 per cent) in that group. However, the values shown are only *estimates* of the *average* amount of nutrients needed by a particular group. Therefore, the term **Estimated Average Requirement (EARs)** is used for the values to show that the specific needs of individuals may vary.

Look at the table below for an example of the RNI of iron for four different groups.

	Adolescents 15–18	Adults 51–59
Male	11.3 mg	8.7 mg
Female	14.8 mg	8.7 mg

Adolescent women need more iron than men because of the loss of blood through menstruation, whereas most women in their 50s have gone through the menopause and so no longer need the extra iron. However, this is not to say that iron is not important for men, as it is needed for muscle development.

Diet through life

Throughout life nutritional needs vary. They will also vary depending on what sex we are. Each life stage and gender can be identified as a specific dietary group. It is important that we understand the varying needs of these groups when designing and making products. The groups can be broadly divided into the following:

- Babies. In the first four months of life, breast or formula milk provides all the nutrients needed. After this, the baby is slowly weaned onto more solid, mashed foods, such as cereals, vegetables and fruit.
- Young children. This group needs to take in more energy (in relation to their size) than they use because they are growing. They need food high in carbohydrates, such as bread and cereals, as well as a mixed, balanced healthy diet, to provide them with the nutrients they need.
- Adolescents. They also need a high-energy intake because they are usually very active and, as puberty sets in, it is an accelerated growth and development stage.
- Adults. The nutritional requirements of an adult vary greatly depending on age, gender, lifestyle and occupation. A less active person will require less energy than a very active one. Both groups still require a balanced diet, but the energy intake will vary to avoid obesity and health-related problems.
- Older people. Energy requirements decrease as people become generally less active. However, it is still essential that older people continue to eat a balanced diet that is interesting and varied. This is an important point as the appetite or desire to eat can often decline as people get older.

Individual needs

The aim of specifying dietary groups and of DRVs, RNIs and EARs, is to minimize the risk of deficiencies in the population as a whole. However, it is important to remember individual needs vary depending on lifestyle and occupation. Other factors may also influence an individual's diet, such as a medical condition, religion, culture, values and beliefs. Special dietary groups include:

- vegetarians
- diabetics (although a healthy, balanced diet should be followed)
- **coeliacs**
- pregnant women
- people following a diet (such as a low fat diet)
- people suffering from high blood pressure or heart problems.

Things to do

1. Compile a food diary to cover one week that details everything that you eat and drink. Does your diet include the recommended balance of nutrients? How healthy are you? Comment on your findings.
2. Design a savoury product for a specific dietary group (choose one of the groups previously described). Explain your design idea and why it meets their needs.

Protein and carbohydrates

Aims

- To understand the importance of protein and carbohydrate in our diet.
- To understand the sources and functions of protein and carbohydrates.

Proteins

Why are proteins important?

Proteins are an essential nutrient in our diet. They are used for body building (growth) and repair. Any protein that the body does not need for growth and repair is used as energy.

Proteins are made up of amino acids. There are 22 different amino acids. Some of these amino acids are very important – they are essential for growth and repair. Proteins that contain all the essential amino acids are said to be of **high biological value (HBV)**. Proteins that lack one or more of the essential amino acids are said to be of **low biological value (LBV)**.

Sources of protein of HBV

Proteins of HBV are mainly found in food products from animal sources such as milk, meat, eggs, fish and cheese.

However, soya beans are also a good source of protein of HBV. As the vegetarian market has grown, a large range of food ingredients made from soya is now available, such as soya mince, **Tofu** and **textured vegetable protein (TVP)**.

All these are sources of protein of high biological value

Another source of protein of HBV available to vegetarians is Quorn, which is the brand name for a food product made from myco-protein (a tiny plant found in soil) and sold as an alternative to meat.

Soya and Quorn are usually bland in taste but, when combined with other ingredients, they absorb their flavours. In fact, it can be difficult to detect the difference in taste between meat and the products made from Quorn and soya. They are also low in fat and provide **non-starch polysaccharides (NSP)** so can be very healthy.

Sources of protein of LBV

Proteins of LBV are mainly found in food products from vegetable sources such as cereals, nuts, beans and pulses.

Alone, these do not supply all the essential amino acids needed by the body. However, they can easily be combined with other foods to provide the right mix, for example, beans on toast.

These vegetable sources of protein have low biological value

Carbohydrates

Why are carbohydrates important?

Carbohydrates provide the body with the energy it needs. We must plan our diet to include enough carbohydrate so that protein can be used for its main function of growth and repair, and not for providing energy.

Carbohydrates are divided into two groups: sugar and starch.

Sugar

Table sugar (sucrose) comes from sugar beet or sugar cane. The beet or cane is collected, crushed and then mixed with water. The liquid is then boiled and sugar crystals are formed.

We eat sugar in many different forms. Some of the sugar we eat is **intrinsic**. This is the sugar that is naturally part of fruit and vegetables. You can't see these sugars so you could say that intrinsic sugars are invisible. **Extrinsic** sugars are those you can see, such as granulated sugar, caster sugar, icing sugar, syrup, treacle and so on. Some extrinsic sugar is less visible. This is the sugar that food manufacturers add to their products, such as processed sauces, cakes, biscuits, soups, soft drinks and so on.

Frequent intake of sugar can lead to obesity and tooth decay. Therefore, it is important that we control the intake of extrinsic sugars and look out for the extrinsic sugars in manufactured foods. Intrinsic sugars are less harmful, as they are less likely to lead to tooth decay and are easier for the body to absorb.

Artificial sweeteners

People are becoming more aware of maintaining a healthy lifestyle and are reviewing what they eat. In response to this, and to government guidelines, many food manufacturers look to reduce the amount of sugar in their products or to substitute it with **artificial sweeteners**. Artificial sweeteners are produced in tablet, liquid or crystal form and are used to provide the sweetness but not the energy value of sugar.

Starch

Foods containing starch include cereals (wheat, rice, oats, maize, barley), bread, yams, pasta and potatoes. Starchy foods are filling and provide us with other nutrients as well as carbohydrates. For example, potatoes contain vitamin C.

Non-starch polysaccharides (NSP)

Non-starch polysaccharides (NSP) are a non-digestible carbohydrate found in plant food. It is more commonly known as fibre. As it cannot be digested it passes straight through the body's system, absorbing water to make our faeces bulky and soft and helping to push out other undigested food. This process is essential to keep the intestine functioning healthily and too little fibre can result in constipation or, in extreme cases, can be a cause of bowel cancer.

NSP is found in a wide variety of foods, such as pulses, fresh and dried fruit, cereals, brown rice and wholemeal bread and pasta.

All these foods provide a good source of fibre

▪ Things to do ▪

1. Design and make a HBV product that contains at least two sources of protein.
2. Design a product that is high in carbohydrate, but in line with dietary goals. Sketch your idea. Label, colour and indicate approximate measurements.
3. Combine a non-animal source of HBV with additional ingredients to prepare an attractive appetizing product. Set up a taste panel and record the opinions of five members of the group.
4. Conduct research into a range of manufactured food products of the same type (for example, baked beans) that have used alternatives to extrinsic sugars. List the alternatives used by the food manufacturers. Why have they used alternatives? How do you think this affects the nutritional value of the product and its taste?

Fats

Aims

- To understand the importance of fat in the diet.
- To understand the sources and functions of fat.

Why is fat important?

Fat in the diet is important for general health and well-being. The function of fat is to:

- provide energy
- surround and protect vital organs in the body
- form an insulating layer under the skin, preserving heat
- give foods texture and flavour
- give the feeling of satiety (fullness)
- carry fat-soluble vitamins A, D, E, K (see pages 10-11).

Why are we always being told to 'eat less fat'?

The 'correct' amount of fat intake in the diet depends on the amount of exercise we take, types of fat we eat and the methods used when preparing and cooking foods. Dietary guidelines say that fat should provide no more than 35 per cent of a person's energy intake.

Amount of exercise

If we are active and take regular exercise, the fat consumed will be used efficiently as an energy source. If not, it will be stored in the body and eventually weight gain will take place.

Sources of fat

Fats come from both plant and animal sources. Animal sources include:

- meat and meat products, for example, lard and suet
- dairy products, for example, milk, butter, cheese and cream
- fish, particularly oily fish, for example, tuna, salmon and pilchard.

Plant sources include:

- some fruits, for example, avocado pears, olives
- nuts and pulses, for example, peanuts and cashews
- seeds, for example, sesame, sunflower and soya.

Types of fat

There are two types of fat: **saturated** and **unsaturated** or **trans fats**.

Saturated fats

Saturated fats include butter, lard, suet and dripping. These types of fats generally come from animal sources.

Some animal sources of fat

Some plant sources of fat

Too much saturated fat can be bad for us and can help increase the amount of blood **cholesterol** in the body. High blood cholesterol is thought to increase the risk of coronary heart disease. The liver produces blood cholesterol using the fat we eat, especially saturated fats. Therefore it is important to reduce the amount of saturated fats we eat to reduce the risk of high blood cholesterol.

Unsaturated fats

Unsaturated fats are split into **monounsaturated** fats and **polyunsaturated** fats, depending on their chemical composition. Unsaturated fats (particularly monounsaturates) can help to reduce blood cholesterol. They are, therefore, a healthy food.

Monounsaturated fats	Found in olive oil, many vegetable oils, most nuts and in very small quantities in fish, lean meat and eggs
Polyunsaturated fats	Found in nuts, grains, seeds and oily fish

Trans fats

Trans fats are produced when food manufacturers pump hydrogen into oil (hydrogenation) in order to make it spreadable at room temperature and to improve its texture and keeping properties. During this process some of the unsaturated fats become saturated and therefore they can be more harmful than unsaturated spreads. Trans fats may be found in margarine.

Many products on the market now have lower fat alternatives

Low fat methods of cooking

Some low fat methods of cooking food include:

- using cooking oil spray to reduce the amount of oil used
- using non-stick pans so less, if any, fat or oil is needed to stop the food sticking to the pan
- steaming, grilling, barbecuing, where very little fat or oil is needed to cook the food
- using low fat alternatives such as low fat spreads.

Low fat options

Food manufacturers have responded to the consumer demand for low fat products so there are now many low fat alternatives on the market. **Recipe engineering** (adapting existing products) takes place to modify some of our favourite foods into healthy, low fat options. Often a low fat variety of the same brand and type of product is produced alongside the 'higher fat' version so people have the choice of which to buy.

When engineering recipes to produce low fat options, food technologists try to maintain the taste and texture of the existing product.

■ Things to do ■

1 Describe six ways of reducing fat in your diet.

2 Visit your supermarket or a supermarket website and conduct a survey of a type of product that has lower fat versions (for example, dairy products or fresh meat products). Set out your findings in a table using the headings below.

Regular product	Does it have a lower fat	How much is the fat content reduced by (%)

3 Design a leaflet using a word-processor or DTP package to promote healthy eating.

The leaflet should be suitable for teenagers and include a recipe that you have engineered into a healthier product by reducing the amount of fat.

Vitamins and minerals

Aims

- To understand the importance of vitamins and minerals in the diet.
- To understand the sources and functions of vitamins and minerals.

Why are vitamins and minerals important?

Vitamins and minerals are essential in the diet for general health and well-being. They protect the body and regulate its functions. However, although this section outlines deficiencies of vitamins and minerals, it is important to note that these are rare in the UK. The tables here give the sources of main vitamins and minerals.

Some vitamins and minerals work in conjunction with each other. For example, vitamin D helps the absorption of calcium into the body and vitamin C helps the absorption of iron.

Fortified foods

Often foods are **fortified** with vitamins and minerals during manufacture. This means the vitamin being added enriches the product. By law, some flours, breads and margarine are fortified. For example, margarine is fortified with vitamins A and D. Fortification may also take place to compensate for nutrient loss during the processing and storage of the product.

Vitamin loss through cooking

To reduce vitamin loss in the domestic environment it is important that foods are prepared and cooked carefully to retain as many of the vitamins as possible. For example, boiling vegetables for too long destroys the water-soluble vitamins present.

Hints and tips

To retain as many water-soluble vitamins as possible when cooking vegetables:

- use as little water as possible
- reduce cooking time
- microwave and steam rather than boil
- use a tight fitting lid when cooking, as vitamins are destroyed when exposed to air.

Vitamins

Vitamins are either water-soluble or fat-soluble.

Water-soluble vitamins

The vitamins in the table below are water-soluble, which means they dissolve in water. They cannot be stored in the body. It is important to remember that the vitamin content of vegetables can be reduced if they are cooked in water.

Fat-soluble vitamins

The vitamins in the table at the top of page 11 are fat-soluble, which means they dissolve in fat and can be stored in the body.

Vitamin	Source	Function	Deficiency
B1 (Thiamin)	Brown rice, liver and kidney	• Functioning and maintenance of the nerves	• Depression • Severe deficiency causes beriberi
B2 (Riboflavin)	Meat, milk, green vegetables	• Normal growth • Required for the release of energy from food	• Failure to grow • Skin disorders • Swollen tongue
C (Ascorbic acid)	Fresh fruit and vegetables, for example, citrus fruits, cabbage, potato, broccoli	• Required for the formation of connective tissue • Helps absorb iron	Severe deficiency can cause scurvy, which affects the gums and the teeth

The sources and functions of selected water-soluble vitamins

Vitamin	Source	Function	Deficiency
A (Retinol and Beta carotene)	Carotene in plant foods, for example, carrots, spinach, prunes and apricots	• Required for the maintenance and health of the skin • Produces a substance called 'visual purple' which helps us see in the dark	Night blindness
D	Liver, oily fish, margarine and sunlight	• Required for the formation of bones and teeth • Helps absorb calcium	• Rickets (poor bone formation affecting children) • Osteomalacia (softening of the bones affecting adults)

The sources and functions of selected fat-soluble vitamins

Minerals

The following table shows the sources and functions of minerals.

Vitamin	Source	Function	Deficiency
Calcium	Milk, yoghurt, cheese, sardines, green vegetables, citrus fruits	It combines with phosphorous to make calcium phosphate, which gives hardness and strength to bones and teeth	• Stunted growth • Can cause rickets
Iron	Liver, kidneys, red meat, bread, potatoes, egg yolk, green vegetables	Combines with protein to form haemoglobin, the red substance in blood that carries oxygen and carbon-dioxide to cells	Anaemia
Sodium	(salt) Cheese, bacon, fish	Maintains water balance in the body	Can cause cramp – deficiency very rare
Flouride	Fish, tea, some drinking water, toothpaste	Strengthening teeth against decay	Tooth decay

The source and functions of selected minerals

Things to do

1. Write a menu consisting of a starter, main course and pudding. The products chosen should be rich in good sources of vitamins and minerals. Produce a chart to explain the importance of the vitamins and minerals in the products you have chosen.
2. What does the term 'fortification' mean?
3. Visit your supermarket or a supermarket's website and conduct a survey of a selection of sweet or savoury products that have been fortified. Set out your findings in a table using the headings opposite. Comment on your findings.

Product	Fortified with with which vitamin/mineral?	Comments

Processing foods 1

Aims

- To understand primary and secondary foods.
- To develop knowledge and understanding of mechanical processing techniques and irradiation.

What is food processing?

Food processing is where raw ingredients are assembled, shaped, formed and presented for consumption. Processing food takes place in both industry and the home. Different techniques are used depending on the end product required and the scale of manufacture.

To understand these processes food can be split into primary and secondary groups.

Primary foods and primary processing

Primary foods, such as the following, receive little or no processing.

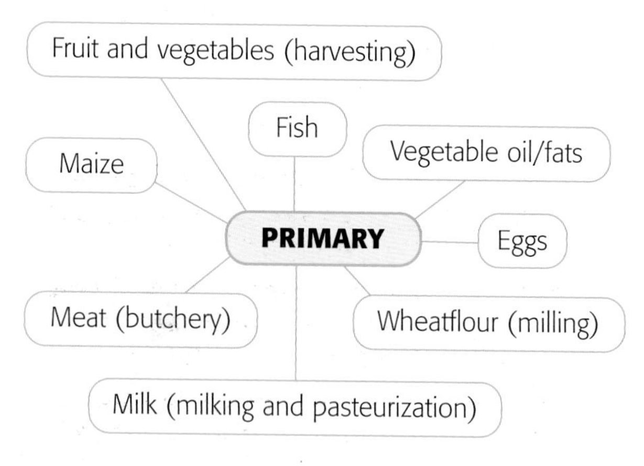

Primary processing is carried out on primary foods to make them suitable for consumption or for conversion into secondary products. For example, meat is processed after slaughter and wheat is processed after harvest to turn it into flour.

Secondary foods and secondary processing

Secondary foods are primary foods that have been processed to form secondary products. For example:

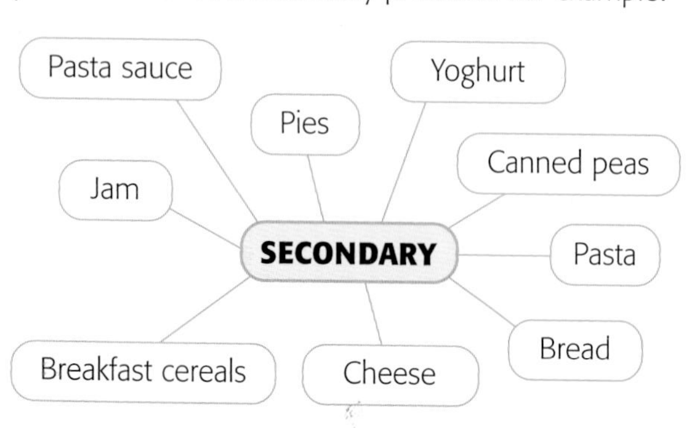

Secondary processing may be defined as the manipulation of primary foods into final products. At each stage of manufacturing a process takes place to convert the raw ingredient into the primary food (primary processing) and then into the secondary food (secondary processing). For example, wheat (a raw ingredient) is processed to make wheatflour (a primary food) that can be processed to become bread (a secondary food).

Primary and secondary processing is used to make bread

Processing food in the home

At home we combine and assemble primary food ingredients with other components to produce savoury or sweet meals. For example, when we make soup we:

- take a selection of vegetables (primary food)
- wash, peel, slice/chop and soften them on a low heat (secondary processing)
- add stock and seasoning, simmer and then blend into a smooth soup (secondary food).

Industrial processing techniques

In industry three main processing techniques are used to produce secondary foods:

1 mechanical **2** heat **3** chemical

(A fourth technique, irradiation, is sometimes used to process foods.)

Mechanical

Mechanical processing includes:

- grading
- cleaning
- sieving
- weighing
- kneading
- extruding
- agitation
- shaping
- mixing
- extracting
- separating

Advancements in technology have greatly reduced the amount of human input in mechanical processes. For example:

- harvesting of crops used to be undertaken manually by the farmer. Now large, efficient labour and time saving equipment (for example, tractors) is used by the farmer to carry out this process.

- mechanical processing is used for grading and cleaning of potatoes (primary food) in the processing of crisps (secondary foods). In the past this would have been done by hand.

Machinery replaces human labour in processing foods

To a certain extent, automated mechanical processing has removed the need for people carrying out repetitive and often very simple tasks. It allows for consistency and accuracy, often using computer programmed and controlled machinery.

The production of breakfast cereals is a good example of mechanical processing.

The cornflake story

The maize (raw material) is gathered by a combine harvester. The grain (primary food) is then milled and transported to the processing plant. Flavourings of malt, sugar and salt are blended and added to the grain. The mixture is funnelled into large cookers where it is sealed in and rotated under steam pressure. It is then dried by being exposed to purified hot air currents for several hours in order to reduce the moisture content before being collected in holding tanks ready for the next stage.

The maize is then flaked under heavy flaking mill rollers and passed through a tumble toaster. The flakes are removed from the toasting process to the filling machine where the cornflakes (secondary food) are weighed, packaged and transported.

Irradiation

Irradiation is the most advanced form of preserving foods and the process has been closely monitored with strict legal controls in place since 1991. If food has been irradiated the following symbol must be displayed.

This symbol must appear on all food that has been irradiated

The aim of irradiation is to reduce food spoilage and delay the natural processes of some foods, for example, the sprouting of potatoes. This can reduce waste and therefore save money. Irradiation exposes food to electron beams or gamma rays, also known as radiation. The energy molecules formed by the radiation destroys **bacteria**. The levels are low enough to kill **micro-organisms**, but not high enough to make the food itself radioactive.

There are seven categories of food that may be legally irradiated, including soft drinks, herbs and spices, potatoes, fresh fruit such as bananas and strawberries, and fresh fish. However, currently in the UK only herbs and spices are irradiated.

Things to do

1. Identify four primary foods and give examples of how they could be processed into secondary food products, both in the home and in industry.
2. Find out examples of where each of the mechanical processing techniques listed might be used. Use books, CD ROMs and the Internet to help you.
3. Read the cornflake story and create a **flow chart** of how the raw material becomes a secondary food.

Processing foods 2

Aims

- To develop knowledge and understanding of heat processing techniques.

Heat processing

This process is concerned with the destruction or reduction of **pathogenic** (harmful) bacteria in order to extend the **shelf life** of the product. Heat processing keeps the food safe and extends its shelf life. It is also used to make food taste better and change its texture.

Types of heat processing include:

- Hot – **pasteurization**, **sterilization**, **UHT**, canning.
- Cold – chilling, cook chilling, **AFD**, freezing, cook freezing.
- Dry – sun drying, commercial spray drying.

Hot methods

These include pasteurization, sterilization, UHT and canning. For example, all these processes are carried out on milk. Milk is a rich source of nutrients and it is an ideal host for the multiplication of bacteria. The aim of heat processing milk is therefore to destroy any pathogenic bacteria present in it.

Pasteurization

In this process, milk is heated to at least 72°C for fifteen seconds to kill bacteria. After this it is rapidly cooled to less than 10°C. This process does not affect the taste of the milk.

Sterilization

Sterilization involves heating the milk to between 105°C and 112°C for 20–40 minutes. This type of milk will remain in a good palatable (pleasant to taste) condition in an unopened bottle for at least a week.

UHT

Ultra heat treatment (UHT) is a form of sterilization where the milk is heated to 132°C for one–three seconds by flowing it over a heated surface. The milk is then completely sterile and, once cooled, packed in a sterile container. This type of milk is affected by the processing and its flavour is very different to pasteurized and sterilized milk. It can be stored unopened for six months, but once opened should be treated in the same way as pasteurized milk.

Canning

Canning is used for preserving a wide variety of foods. Cans are made from steel and then coated with a thin layer of tin to stop them going rusty. Canning preserves foods by preventing air coming into contact with the food. Some micro-organisms need air to live and grow. Other micro-organisms can survive without air so cans have to be heated to destroy these. Examples of food that can be canned include soups, beans, tomatoes, meat, sausages, sponge puddings, pasta sauce and some vegetables.

The canning process involves the following stages:

1. cleaning and preparation
2. blanching
3. filling
4. sealing
5. sterilization
6. cooling
7. drying
8. labelling.

Cold methods

Cold methods are used as a way to preserve foods because reducing the temperature either slows down or prevents the growth of bacteria. Cold methods include chilling, cook chilling, AFD, freezing and cook freezing.

Chilling

This is where products are kept at temperatures below 8°C. Salads, sandwiches, cream and pâté are examples of foods that are chilled to extend shelf life.

Cook chilling

Cook chilling involves preparing the raw ingredients, cooking them and then chilling the product rapidly to between 0°C–3°C within 90 minutes. The product must then be stored at just above 0°C to prevent bacteria multiplying. All cook chill products must be thoroughly reheated before eating. This process can be used to produce products like lasagne, sweet 'n' sour dishes, pies, meat loaf and vegetable bakes.

Cook chill technology is extremely convenient for consumers, as all they have to do is reheat the product. Moreover, the process does not affect the food quality and the product retains its colour, flavour, texture, shape and nutritional value.

AFD

Accelerated freeze-drying (AFD) is a method of drying frozen foods in a vacuum. The ice is driven off as water vapour. Products that have been processed in this way are usually light in weight, easy to store and, when reconstituted with water, in most cases the physical, sensory and nutritional qualities of the product are not affected. Examples of AFD processed products are coffee, instant tea and some fruits.

Freezing

Freezing is one of the most commonly used methods of preserving foods and it is used in the home as well as in industry. The domestic freezer operates at temperatures between −18°C and −25°C. Industrial freezers operate at a lower temperature than this (−29°C) to ensure high quality and a long storage life.

Frozen foods are kept in good condition because micro-organisms are dormant (inactive) at low temperatures.

Not all foods are suitable for freezing because of their high water content, for example, watermelon. When these products are thawed they can often lose their shape and texture because freezing ruptures the cell walls.

Some foods are not suitable for freezing

Cook freezing

Cook freezing is a process where the food is cooked, then frozen at a low temperature (-18°C or below). It is stored in the freezer compartments in supermarkets and then can be stored in the home freezer. The products made using this process are similar to the cook chill ones, the difference being that they can be stored for longer periods of time. Like cook chill foods the product must be reheated by the consumer until it is piping hot (always following the instructions on the label).

Drying methods

Drying methods involves the removal of moisture without which micro-organisms are unable to multiply. This makes drying an effective method of preservation. Examples of dried foods are pasta, rice, fruits, vegetables, flour, pulses and fish. Two drying methods are sun drying and commercial spray drying.

Sun drying

Sun drying is a traditional method of drying. The food is laid out in containers to 'dry' in the sun. Obviously, this method is only suitable for hot climate countries, such as Italy, where sun dried tomatoes are a specialty.

In some countries fresh fish is caught in the morning haul and laid out on the harbour to dry. Hygiene is obviously an issue, as the fish can easily become contaminated while it is drying.

Sun dried tomatoes

Commercial spray drying

Commercial spray drying is commonly used for the drying of milk. This process involves spraying a liquid (milk) into a cylinder of hot air. The liquid enters and evaporates which then leaves a fine powder milk. Dried milk can be used as an ingredient or re-hydrated with water.

Things to do

1. Set up a taste panel using pasteurized, sterilized and UHT milk. Design a star diagram with appropriate descriptors. Taste the milk and fill in your star diagram. Evaluate your findings.
2. Investigate the effects of freezing on a range of ingredients. Record the colour, aroma, texture, volume and overall appearance of the products before they are frozen and put your results in a table. Securely wrap each product and label clearly.

   Freeze for one week and then defrost. Now go back to your record table and evaluate the product again using the same criteria. Using examples, describe any differences you find in the taste and texture of the foods.

Processing foods 3

Aims

- To develop knowledge and understanding of chemical processing techniques.
- To understand the advantages and disadvantages of processing food.

Chemical processing

Chemical processing has been used for many years in the manufacture of food products. It involves using chemicals or **additives** in food manufacture.

Additives

Additives can be natural, artificial or nature identical (made to the same chemical formula as natural additives, for example, riboflavin). They are used in many food products to preserve them and to enhance their colour, flavour and texture. Additives are identified by E numbers. The E number indicates that an additive has been approved for use throughout the European Union. All additives, if present, must be listed on food labelling.

Colours

Colours are additives used to improve the appearance of food or to replace colour lost during processing, for example, in canned vegetables, soft drinks, biscuits, dessert mixes, sausages and gravy browning. They can come from artificial or natural sources and are identified by E numbers 100–199.

Preservatives

Preservatives help extend the shelf life of a product, for example, in yoghurts, processed cheese slices, fruit-based pie fillings, jam and salad cream. They are numbered using E numbers 200–299.

Some additives used for preservation have been around for a long time and include:

- vinegar – pickled onions, cabbage and eggs
- salt – salting canned foods, meat and fish
- sugar – jamming (making jam)
- alcohol – peaches in brandy, cherries in kirsch.

As well as acting as preservatives each of these additives lends a distinctive taste and texture to food.

Antioxidants

Antioxidants can be natural (for example, vitamins C and E) or artificial. These prevent the fat-soluble vitamins A and D, oils and fats from joining with oxygen in the air and making the product turn rancid. They also prevent some foods from turning brown (for example, fruit) when exposed to air. They are used in products, such as fruit drinks, vegetable oils, cereal based foods, soup mixes, stock cubes and cheese spread. They are identified by E numbers 300–321.

Emulsifiers and stabilizers

Emulsifiers and stabilizers create an emulsion between oil and water, which prevents them separating when stored. They are used in low fat spreads, salad creams, meringue mixes, sweet pickle, brown sauce and mousse mixes. They are identified by E numbers 322–499.

Flavourings and flavour enhancers

Flavouring and flavour enhancers enhance the flavour of the product, for example, crisps and soup. They can be natural (herbs and spices) or artificial (monosodium glutamate).

Artificial sweeteners

Artificial sweeteners are substituted for sugar in low calorie drinks, sugar-free chewing gum and sugar-free confectionary. Examples include saccharine, aspartame, and thaumatin.

Raising agents

Raising agents increases the volume and enhance the texture of food, for example, in cakes or bread. Raising agents can either be natural (yeast) or chemical (bicarbonate of soda). For more information on raising agents see pages 40-1.

Thickeners and gelling agents

Thickeners and gelling agents improve and thicken the texture of food by forming a gel, for example, pectin in jam.

Acidity regulators/buffers

These control the acidity levels in food by altering or stabilizing the acid level, for example, in pickles.

Anti-caking agents

These stop the formation of lumps of powder in liquid and are used in biscuits, coca products and skimmed milk powder.

Bacteria

Some bacteria produce acids when placed in foods. This acid then lowers the **pH level** of the food and this prevents the growth of other micro-organisms. For example, adding bacillus lactus to milk makes yoghurt.

Things to do

1. Collect a range of food labels and study the ingredients list. Identify which products contain additives and explain the function of each one.
2. Explain how bacteria can act as a preservative.
3. List five reasons why additives are used in the manufacturing process.

Advantages and disadvantages of processing foods

Advantages	Disadvantages
Mechanical processing Can process raw materials and primary foods into secondary foods quickly, in large volume and to a consistent standard. This consequently reduces the amount of time and cost needed to process foods.	Costly equipment is needed to process the foods as well as staff trained in operating machinery and health and safety issues. Mechanical processing may affect the taste of some foods.
Irradiation Reduces the amount of harmful bacteria in food and kills any insects and pests. It also slows down natural processes, such as fruit over-ripening. All this reduces waste and consequently can save the manufacturer and the consumer money.	Food may appear safe to eat, even though not all the bacterial **toxins** have been destroyed. Some nutrients are lost during irradiation. Consumers may fear exposure to radiation.
Heat processing Prolongs the shelf life of food, allowing food manufacturers to produce and distribute a wide variety of products. Useful in mass catering (for example, airlines) and convenient for the consumer.	Very important to monitor and control temperatures otherwise any micro-organisms present would have time to multiply. Heat processing may affect the taste of some foods.
Chemical processing Enhances the taste, flavour and texture of foods as well as preserving them and extending their shelf life. This makes food attractive and tasty to eat.	Some natural and artificial additives can cause allergic reactions in people.

Properties and characteristics of foods 1

Aims

- To understand the properties and working characteristics of food as a material and how different functional properties affect finished products.

Food is a material with many functional properties and working characteristics. It is important to understand these when designing or enhancing food products to enable successful modification. The functions of food used in manufacturing include:

thickening	setting	crystallization
fermentation	fortification	foaming
tenderizing	**aeration**	solutions
laminating	browning	binding
shortening.		

Thickening

The main thickeners used in food products are flours and starchy vegetables (for example, potatoes). They are used to improve and thicken the consistency of food products, such as sauces and soups that would be too thin otherwise. The thickeners used are all starchy foods. When starch is heated in liquid it goes through a process called gelatinization, that is, the starch granules absorb water and swell. At 80°C the granules rupture, releasing the starch. The starch forms a gel that thickens the liquid. When cooled the gel solidifies (sets).

Examples of thickeners

- Flour can be used to thicken soups.
- Cornflour is often used to thicken sauces.
- Potatoes are added to some soups as they thicken and bulk the mixture.

Setting

In order to create the desired consistency and texture in some food products a gelling agent is used to make it set. Setting agents include gelatine, pectin, cornflour and rennet.

Examples of setting

- Gelatine is a transparent, odourless and tasteless setting agent. It is produced from boiling the bones and tissues of cattle and sold commercially in powder or sheet form. When mixed in warm water, it dissolves and swells. The protein molecules in gelatine trap water to form a gel. As gelatine cools down it thickens and sets. It is used to set jellies and mousses. Agar and carrageen (seaweed) are suitable alternatives for vegetarians.
- Pectin is naturally present in fruits. When the fruits (which are acidic), sugar and water are boiled together in jam making, they make a gel. This is because the pectin molecules trap the fruit, water and sugar and hold them together. The gel will set as it cools. This enables us to spoon and spread marmalades and jam. Pectin is also available commercially in liquid or powder form.

The pectin has produced a setting gel that suspends the fruit in the jam

- Cornflour is used to set cold sauces and blancmanges. The starch granules in cornflour, when mixed with liquid, form a gel that can act as a setting agent as well as a thickener. It should never be added directly into the mixture, as it will form lumps that will not dissolve. Instead a paste must be formed first by mixing it with liquid. This paste can then be stirred into the mixture and will set it when chilled.
- Rennet (see pages 68-9) is a dilute form of the **enzyme** rennin found in calves' stomachs. It is used in the cheese-making process, as it acts to set milk, forming soft curds. When the curds are formed there is excess liquid left over (whey) which is drained away. Then the curds are processed to form different types of cheeses. Rennet derived from vegetable sources is available for vegetarians.

Gluten in flour

The proteins present in flour are converted into another protein called gluten when water is added to the flour. When flour mixtures are cooked, the gluten sets in strands, forming a structure that provides the shape of products like bread.

Fermentation

Fermentation is a biological process involving a series of chemical reactions. It occurs when gas and heat are produced by micro-organisms (bacteria or yeast) as they convert organic material into the energy needed to multiply. Fermentation is an anaerobic process (for example, the micro-organisms can live without oxygen). The chemical changes that take place help to preserve some food products (for example, yoghurt) and help bread to rise.

Examples of fermentation

- Fermentation using yeast produces carbon dioxide, causing bread to rise or 'prove' during bread making, giving it its volume and structure.
- Fermentation is used to produce alcoholic beverages. Yeast converts into alcohol and carbon dioxide. Fermentation is beneficial because the alcohol and carbon dioxide help to preserve the beverage.

Fortification

Products are fortified (enriched) to replace or compensate for any amount of vitamins or minerals lost during the manufacturing process. Fortification is used to make the nutritional value of food similar to the original ingredient, or to ensure a sufficient amount of specific vitamin or mineral is present.

Examples of fortification

- Commercial fruit juices are often fortified with vitamin C so that they have the same vitamin content as freshly squeezed orange juice.
- Textured vegetable protein (TVP) is often fortified with iron and vitamin B complex so that it has a similar nutritional value as meat.
- Yoghurt is sometimes fortified with vitamins A and D to replace nutrients lost during processing.

Tenderizing

Tenderizing is used in the preparation of meat for sale and consumption. Meat is comprised of muscle fibres and connective tissue. The older the animal, the longer the connective tissues and the thicker the muscle fibres. Tenderizing breaks down the tissue and the muscle to make the meat more tender (less tough). This can be achieved by:

- Marinating. Before cooking, the meat is marinated (soaked) in a liquid. For example, meat can be marinated in lemon juice mixed with olive oil and herbs or in a can of tomatoes with soy sauce, garlic and honey. The enzymes in the liquid will penetrate and soften the tissue and, at the same time, infuse it with flavour.
- Ageing. This is mainly used for 'game' meats, for example, duck, pheasant, grouse and venison. The meat is hung up and the micro-organisms in it begin the process of decay. This causes the connective tissue and muscles to loosen, making the meat tenderer.

This game is going through the ageing process

Things to do

1. Produce a flow diagram to show the process of the gelatinization of starch granules.
2. Design your own marinade and explain how it might tenderize your meat.

Properties and characteristics of foods 2

Aims

- To understand the properties and working characteristics of food as a material, and how different functional properties affect finished products.

Aeration

Aeration involves introducing air or carbon dioxide into a mixture. It will result in a 'light' mixture often required in food preparation. Types of aeration include:

- Mechanical. This is where a mixture is beaten to add air to it. Mechanical methods include whisking, beating, sieving, folding, creaming (butter and sugar) and rubbing in, for example, cakes.
- Chemical. This is where a chemical agent is used in the mixture. When mixed with liquid and heated the agent produces carbon dioxide. This expands and raises the mixture. Chemical raising agents include baking powder, yeast and bicarbonate of soda.
- Steam. Steam is produced during the baking process of some products. It is produced when the liquid present in the mixture heats up and evaporates, turning into steam that raises the mixture. This method of aeration is used to produce Choux pastry, batters and flaky pastry.

Laminating

Laminating involves adding a layer of another ingredient to the food product to:

- add texture, colour and flavour to it
- to increase its nutritional content
- to protect it if it is a delicate food.

This can be a coating or a glaze.

Coating

Coating can enhance the appearance, texture, colour and taste of the finished product. Examples include sugar on doughnuts, batter on a piece of fish or breadcrumbs on a fillet of meat.

Glazing

Glazing can add an attractive finish to a product, improving its texture and appearance. Types of glazes include:

- sugar and water mixed together, brushed over hot, sweet pastries to form a sticky layer
- egg yolk brushed over scones to create a golden brown appearance
- egg wash (a mixture of milk and egg) brushed over pastry to create a shiny appearance
- two tablespoons of jam warmed in a saucepan can be brushed over sweet flans to create a shiny, sticky layer
- honey can be used to glaze ham prior to baking to add flavour, texture, colour and aroma
- fast-setting jelly can be poured over a fruit flan. Often it is coloured to compliment the fruit being used
- aspic (a clear jelly made from gelatine and stock) forms a jelly substance when cooked with meat and cooled. The jelly substance produced can be found in pork pies and canned Spam meat.

A breadcrumb coating has been added to this chicken

Aspic is used as a laminate in pork pies

Browning

Browning is the term used to describe colour changes in foods. This affects their appearance. There are four causes of browning described below.

Non-enzymic browning

This is where simple sugars (carbohydrates) react with the protein in the food. This acts to brown the product when cooked in a dry heat. An example of this is when meat which is dry is cooked (for example, in an oven) it turns a golden brown.

Enzymic browning

This occurs when some fruit and vegetables are cut or sliced and exposed to the air. The enzymes present in the food react with the oxygen in the air and turn the cut surface brown. Adding an acid to the cut surface, such as lemon juice, can prevent this.

Caramelization

This is the heating of a sugar to a temperature above its melting point. The sugar thickens and turns brown, producing a toffee-like flavour and consistency. For example, when set, caramelized sugar will form toffee around an apple. **Caramelization** is also often used in sugar spinning (for example, candy floss) or to form a caramel topping on crème brûlée. Its crunchy texture and sweet taste is very appealing.

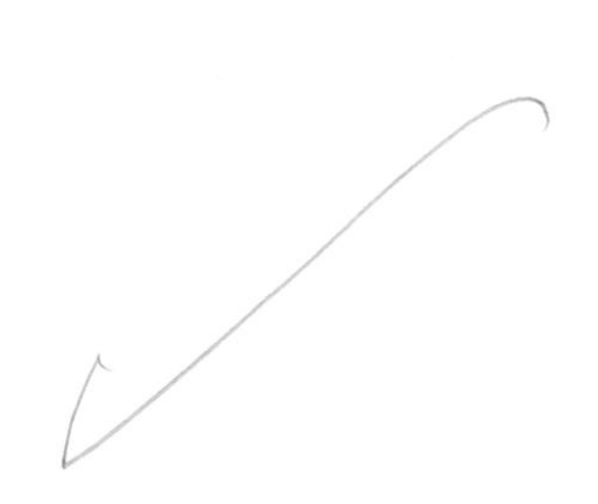

Dextrinization

Dextrinization occurs when, in a dry heat, starch is turned into dextrin (a simple sugar) that caramelizes and turns brown. Examples include toasting or grilling bread.

Dextrinization makes toast turn brown

■ Things to do ■

1. Give practical examples of mechanical aeration.
2. Explain why laminating may be used in the manufacturing process. Give some examples of laminated foods.
3. Describe the difference between coating and glazing.
4. List the four forms of browning, giving examples for each one identified.

Properties and characteristics of foods 3

Aims

- To understand the properties and working characteristics of food as a material and how different functional properties affect finished products.

Binding

Binding is an important stage in the assembly of some products. It is the process of combining dry ingredients together with another ingredient so that a shape can be formed. When binding takes place the ingredients are being drawn together. Some ingredients used for binding include:

- water – binds together flour and fat for pastry
- egg – binds the ingredients in the production of burgers. The egg will coagulate (the proteins in the egg white and yolk are changed by the heat) when cooked and hold the ingredients together
- flour and breadcrumbs – can bind moist ingredients, for example, when **moulding** and shaping burgers
- milk – can be used to bind raw ingredients together to form a soft dough, for example, in scone making.

Shortening

In order to make baked products such as shortcrust pastry and shortcakes soft and crumbly, fat is added as a shortening.

Fat, when mixed with flour, covers the flour particles. As a result, when liquid is added to the flour, it cannot develop gluten to make an elastic mix. This is because the fat covering the flour particles stops them absorbing water. The resulting mixture when cooked forms a crumbly, flaky and tender pastry.

Foaming

Foaming is important in some food products to provide structure, lightness and texture. It occurs when a gas is dispersed into another ingredient. This gas can be incorporated:

- by beating or whisking a substance (for example, beating egg whites adds air to them, creating a foam that could be used to make meringues)
- by chemical reaction (for example, the yeast in bread releases carbon dioxide, which is trapped by the gluten, creating a foam).

Egg white foam

Egg white foam may be folded into a mixture to make it light and full of air, for example, for soufflés and mousses. If egg yolk is added to the foam it reduces the volume of the foam and the amount of bubbles by at least two thirds. This makes the foam unstable because the fat in the egg yolk prevents the protein in the egg white forming a protective layer around the air bubbles.

Folding in egg white foam to make a soufflé

How meringues are formed

The egg white foams when whisking or beating has added air. The egg white protein forms a protective layer around the air bubbles. This stabilizes the foam. When heated, the air bubbles grow bigger and the egg white protein coagulates to make a solid network of bubbles. As a result, the foam changes from a liquid into a solid and a permanent meringue is formed. This is an irreversible change.

Solutions and crystallization

Dissolving another substance in a liquid creates solutions. A solution is made up of two elements: the solute (the substance which is dissolved) and the solvent (the liquid).

Water and sugar is a common solution that is used in the manufacture of confectionary. This is because this solution allows crystallization to take place, resulting in the formation of solid sugar crystals.

How does crystallization take place?

The sugar solution has a higher boiling point than water. As the boiling point goes above 100°C the water in the solution evaporates. This leaves a higher concentration of sugar behind, which has formed into crystals. The higher the boiling point, the more water evaporates and the harder the crystals produced.

Boiling point	Uses
115°C	Making marzipan
143°C	Making sugar baskets by pulling the sugar crystals into shape
177°C	Making caramel which can be used as an additive for colouring and flavouring

Uses of crystallized sugar

Other solutions

Another solution commonly used in the food industry is the solution of water, gelatine and salt. When boiled at 100°C this solution forms a jelly, which cools and set around the meat, for example, in the production of pork pies.

■ Things to do ■

1. Make two batches of pastry: one using butter and the other using margarine. Set up a tasting panel to comment on the shortness of both pastries. Which is shorter? Why do you think this is the case? Which one tastes better?
2. Describe what happens to an egg white foam when it is heated.

Choice and fitness-for-purpose 1

Aims

- To understand that the choice of food material depends on the needs of the user, the presentation of the food, storage properties, shelf life and cost.

User needs

When designing products many factors must be taken into consideration to ensure that the product will be marketable. A marketable product will meet consumer needs (that is, the needs of the **target market group**) and consequently sell, creating a profit for the manufacturer and retailer.

For example, a new product that is similar to other products, but more expensive and with a short shelf life, is unlikely to be successful. This is because there is no reason for the consumer to switch to the new product. However, if one of these factors is different, for example, if the product is offering something new that the consumer wants, it is cheaper or can be stored longer, then this product has a **competitive advantage** that may allow it to sell successfully.

An example of a new product that was successful in a highly competitive market is *Sunny Delight*. It entered the soft drinks market a few years ago, marketing itself as a 'healthy' alternative to traditional fizzy soft drinks. Its target group was children and their parents, as the manufacturers saw a gap in the market for this sort of drink for children. Consequently it sold successfully.

Sunny Delight is an example of a product that met the needs of its target group

Factors affecting the choice of foods

As well as meeting the needs of consumers, there are a number of other factors that affect the choice and fitness-for-purpose of food materials. These must be considered when designing a new product or modifying an existing one. These factors are shown in the diagram below. It is important to remember these factors do not act alone. It is the relationship between them that results in the ultimate choice of materials for the product.

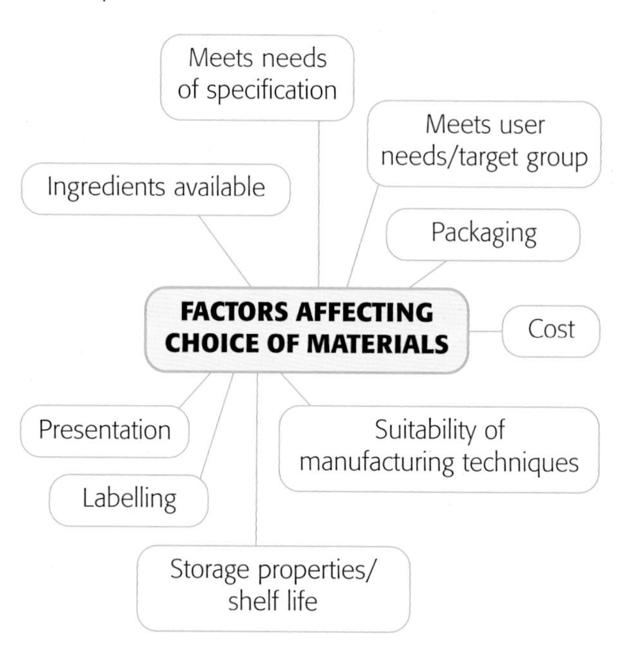

Presentation

The presentation of a product is essential to catch the eye of the consumer. The **sensory characteristics** (appearance, colour, texture, taste and aroma) of the product must be acceptable and attractive in order to encourage the consumer to buy.

Food technologists work very hard to ensure the sensory characteristics of the product are right. In the development stage of creating a new product, or when modifying an existing one, the testing of these sensory characteristics will be rigorous to ensure the product meets the specification. A cross section of people and/or the target consumer group is used to taste and comment on the product. The test results are used to guide any modifications needed to improve the product, whether it be choosing a different ingredient or altering the amounts of ingredients used.

Storage properties and shelf life

The shelf life of a product is the length of time it will remain edible and safe to eat if stored as recommended by the manufacturer. Its storage properties are the conditions in which it should be stored so it does not spoil before the end of its shelf life. Both of these factors are dependent on the ingredients of the product and how it is processed and packaged.

Storage

Foods should always be stored according to the manufacturer's instructions. This means from point of manufacture to when it is eaten. For example, as soon as a cook chill product is produced, the following storage methods apply:

- Dispatch room – ready for transportation. Must be stored at a temperature below 3°C.
- Transportation – must be transported in refrigerated lorries at a temperature below 1°C.
- Storage at retailers – must be stored in refrigerated compartments at a temperature below 3°C.
- Storage at home – must be kept in a fridge at a temperature below 3°C.

Most cook chill products can be stored for no longer than five days, including the day of manufacture. Therefore, these products have a shelf life of five days. Many consumers want to have as much storage time as possible (rather than going to the supermarket every day) and how long they can keep something may affect their buying decisions. This means another important consideration for manufacturers of cook chill and fresh products is logistics, getting the product onto supermarket shelves as quickly as possible from point of manufacture.

Therefore, we can begin to see how factors affecting choice of materials are linked (in this case the link between storage time and user needs).

Shelf life

The shelf life of a product is displayed on the packaging using a date stamp. This is either a 'use by' or 'best before' date. A 'use by' date is used on chilled foods that should be stored in a fridge. After this date the food is considered harmful to eat. A 'best before' date is used on most other products (including frozen) and means that the product is best before the date shown (though not necessarily harmful after it). For products that do not have packaging, for example, loose fruit and vegetables, it is a question of judgement on the part of the consumer. It is quite easy to determine by sight and touch if a fruit or vegetable has passed its best (for example, it might be going soft or browning).

Manufacturers are keen to extend the shelf life of their products, as this means there are more opportunities for sale before the product becomes inedible and wasted. This is why the choice of ingredients to use can depend on how their properties can extend the shelf life of a product, for example, by adding preservatives (see pages 16-17). Also the choice of processing techniques may depend on how they can extend shelf life, for example, irradiation (see pages 12-13).

Victoria sandwich cake

A mass-produced Victoria sandwich cake provides an example of how products can be modified for large-scale production by choosing ingredients for a particular property they have. As well as the traditional ingredients of egg, flour, sugar and aft, some other ingredients have been added. A homemade sponge might have a shelf life of five days. However, this mass-produced cake has a longer shelf life because it has been modified by including ingredients that prolong shelf life. These include:

- Emulsifiers – keeps the mixed fat and oil from separating in water
- Preservatives – extends the shelf life of the cake
- Water – creates steam during baking. The steam enhances the texture of the cake by giving it a light, open texture
- Salt – develops the flavour
- Glycerine – gives added moisture during shelf life of the cake.

■ Things to do ■

1. How would you ensure that the presentation of a food product you had designed met the needs of your target market group?
2. Look at the information on a cook freeze piece of packaging. What is its shelf life and storage properties? How does this differ from a cook chill product?
3. Look at the ingredients of a mass-produced food product of your choice. What ingredients have been added which you would not use in a one-off recipe? Explain why you think each had been added.

Choice and fitness-for-purpose 2

Aims

- To understand that the choice of packaging materials depends on the properties of foods they contain and on the labelling requirements of packaging.
- To understand the choice of food material depends on their cost and the manufacturing techniques needed to produce them for home and small **batch production**.

Packaging

Packaging has both an aesthetic and practical function in the manufacture of food products. For food manufacturers it is an important consideration for a number of reasons. These can be split into those that apply to every type of packaging and those that apply to some packaging.

Every type of packaging

- To protect the food product from damage in transportation and storage.
- To keep bacteria and dirt away from the food.
- To attract consumers to look at and hopefully buy the product.
- To increase the shelf life of the product.
- To contain the food product.
- To provide the consumer with information about the product.
- To prevent tampering with the product.
- To be efficient to produce.

Some types of packaging

- To be good heat conductors to enable reheating.
- To be suitable for microwaving.
- To be recycled.

On the whole, the type of packaging depends on the type of product manufactured, that is, the type of packaging used must be suitable for the product. For example, canned products are packaged in cans in order to extend shelf life of the food (see pages 36-7). Cans are easily stacked and are therefore a convenient way of storing the food on supermarket shelves without taking up too much shelf space.

However, in order to attract more sales, food manufacturers are constantly looking at ways to make their products different from other similar products on the market. One way they can do this is through innovations in packaging. For example, the round teabag or the cans of food that have a ring pull to make them more convenient. The problem with innovative packaging is that it is soon copied by the competition. Therefore, it is mainly through the graphic design on the packaging that manufacturers are able to differentiate their product from the rest.

Labelling

Labelling on food packaging informs and advises the consumer. For manufacturers it is a legal requirement to include the following on a food label:

- name of the product
- ingredients (in descending order of proportion used)
- net weight (unless under 5g)
- name and address of the manufacturer
- 'use by' or 'best before' date
- storage instructions
- instructions for use.

Cost

Cost is a very important factor to consider when designing products for manufacture and sale. When selling any product it must make a profit otherwise the manufacturer would go out of business. Therefore, when making choices about which ingredients, processes and packaging to use in the manufacture of a food product, the manufacturing cost must be lower than the amount of money made from selling it.

The process of costing a product is a balancing act. In food design and manufacture the following costs must be taken into consideration:

- ingredients
- set up and initial design costs
- labour
- packaging
- factory and distribution
- marketing and advertising
- retailer's cost and profit.

If the product is made in large quantities, these costs, in proportion to an individual item produced, will be reduced. For example, ingredients and packaging in bulk are cheaper per item.

Therefore, if the manufacturer is confident that it can sell the product in large quantities, it is more economical to produce large batches of the product than small batches. However, problems arise when sales forecasts are not achieved. This leaves the manufacturer with a lot of unsold product and costs that have not been met by sales.

Costing a product is more of a risk with new products, as there is no sales history. With well-established products, manufacturers can be fairly confident of accurate cost planning.

Pricing

Another important factor is of course the selling price. It might be tempting to increase the selling price to cover costs and make a profit. However, when deciding on a price for a product the following factors need to be considered:

- the target market group – how much would they be willing to spend on the product?
- the price of similar products on the market
- where it is going to be sold.

Basically, if the product is overpriced it may not sell so the market limits the price manufacturers can put on a product.

Example of costing a product

If you were making a batch of twelve items where the cost of ingredients was £3, the costs might look like the following table:

Manufacturing costs	Price	Proportion of total costs
Ingredients	£3.00	30%
Labour	£0.50	5%
Packaging	£0.50	5%
Factory and distribution	£2.00	20%
Marketing and advertising	£1.00	10%
Retailer's cost and profit	£3.00	30%
Total	£10.00	100%

The cost per item would then be £10 divided by 12, which would be approximately 83.3p per item made. Therefore, in order to make a profit, you would need to price each item above this cost. If this price were unacceptable to the consumer, you would have to look at reducing costs. However, this might have an affect on how the product sells, for example, using alternative, cheaper ingredients or reducing your advertising costs. Therefore, it is clear why the cost per batch has an important influence on the choice of materials used.

Manufacturing techniques for the home and small batch production

The choice of manufacturing techniques depends on their suitability for the food product being made. Depending on whether a food product is being made at home or in industry, different manufacturing techniques are used. The table below highlights examples of these differences when making a cherry bakewell tart.

Things to do

1. Outline the factors that need to be considered when packaging a cook chill product.
2. Collect one savoury and one sweet recipe. Cost each recipe as if you were making a batch of 100 in industry. Use the same proportions as used in the table on this page.

   How much would the price of each individual portion need to be in order to make a profit?
3. Using the table that highlights comparisons between manufacturing techniques on this page, and the case studies on pages 66-77, create your own table of difference between home and industrial manufacturing techniques. For the comparison use a food product of your choice.

Industry	Home
Assembling raw ingredients Computerized machinery to accurately weigh each component	Each component added by weighing on scales, using level tablespoons and checking visually
Mixing Large scale mixers used	Domestic equipment used, for example, electric hand whisk, food processor, blender
Cutting Industrial cutters used to slice accurately without wasting the product	Shaped individual cutters or knife used to cut blocks
Slicing Large scale slicers used to slice accurately without wasting the product	Sharp knife used
Glazing Spray guns used to release the glaze evenly	Pastry brush and jug containing the egg wash/water
Piping Large scale machine used controlling the amount of mixture to be piped	Piping bag and nozzle filled with cream.

Choice and fitness-for-purpose 3

Aims

- To understand how to scale up recipes for batch production.
- To understand that the choice of food materials depends on the specification.

Scaling up recipes

When **scaling up** recipes for large-scale production in industry, food technologists must consider adding additional ingredients to maintain flavour, texture, colour and the shelf life of a product. This process takes place in a test kitchen, where small batches are often produced to see whether production in quantity affects the sensory characteristics of the product. After testing (see pages 44-7) modifications may have to be made to the product.

The food technologist also has to consider large scale mixing and baking temperatures, and the effect these may have on whether the product meets the specification. Each stage of the **system** has to be carefully considered before a full batch is produced.

In the home environment many people batch produce to save time and money. To scale up a recipe the proportion and ration of ingredients simply need to be multiplied.

Example of scaling up a recipe for four people

The recipe for lasagne rolls is:

- 2 x 15ml spoons of vegetable oil
- 8 fresh lasagne sheets
- 120g button mushrooms
- 250g boned chicken breast
- 30g margarine
- 30g flour
- 140ml milk
- 120g cheddar cheese.

To serve eight people simply double the mixture, for example, 240g of mushrooms and so on. To serve 32, multiply each ingredient quantity by eight, for example, 960g of mushrooms and so on. However, be careful because large quantities of some ingredients might behave differently or might become very expensive. You may need to adapt the recipe for very large quantities.

Scaling up the recipe is the easy part. Before producing a scaled up recipe at home you need to consider:

- equipment – size and quantity available
- time and ability to assemble – it is often difficult to mix large mixtures to achieve the correct consistency, so what electrical pieces of equipment could be used to save time, labour and encourage accuracy?
- cooking – time and oven, hob or microwave space
- quality – ensuring all the products are of the same quality and standard
- cost – buying ingredients in bulk can be an expensive initial cost but, in the long term, can save money as buying in bulk is cheaper per individual item. This is particularly true if you buy products in season when they are cheaper.

Buying in bulk is cheaper than buying a small amount

Design specifications

This is generated using an analysis of the data gathered from market research. It allows the food technologist to generate ideas that are suitable.

Product specifications

This is very detailed and reflects the sensory and physical characteristics of the product.

Manufacturing specifications

This is utilized in the manufacturing of the product idea. It is a very detailed document that instructs the

Criteria	Details
Target group	Family
Nutritional requirements	Low fat, for example, lean mincemeat, skimmed milk for the sauce, low fat cheese, sauce blended without fat
Retail price	£3.99
Size	Similar to Findus brand product for a family size lasagne
Method of production	Suitable for batch production, using **standard components**
Storage	Suitable for freezing
Method of reheating	Microwave/oven cook
Flavour	Rich and herby, with a cheesy flavoured topping
Colour	Golden brown topping, rich meaty brown interior
Garnish	Fresh herbs, for example, parsley, basil, oregano, sliced tomatoes. Grated cheese, for example, parmesan
Appearance	To appear like a Findus brand product, for example, a layered effect
Quality	An accurate consistently produced main course with a high quality finish
Safety	To follow health and safety regulations for a cook chill product
Packaging	Bright, attractive and suitable for the designed product, for example, use of microwaveable tray in interior packaging
Labelling	By law and additional information

manufacturer how to produce the product, for example, the quantities required, time to mix, length of cooking, method of production and packaging and labelling.

Modifying a recipe

Often the design specification is modified to create a prototype that is slightly different from the original product idea. This type of modification is called recipe engineering. The specification could be altered to modify the nutritional profile of the product, for example, to reduce the saturated fat content, or be altered to make it suitable for vegetarians or coeliacs.

Reasons for modification

Manufacturers might modify an existing product:

- to adapt a recipe for larger/smaller scale production
- to extend the product range, for example, producing a cheaper alternative for a low income target market by using cheaper ingredients
- to respond to lifestyle changes, for example, convenience products such as ready meals
- to create new product ideas
- to respond to what the competition is developing
- to enhance the qualities of an existing product, for example, 'new improved' recipe
- to increase or maintain sales of a product when its life cycle is coming to an end
- to meet the needs of the user group, for example, increasing consumer awareness of what is healthy to eat.

■ Things to do ■

1. Identify a product range, for example, breakfast cereal bars, and develop ides that could be made to extend the product range.
2. Using a selection of cookery books, select a recipe and then modify the recipe to produce a lower coast alternative.
3. Using the specification for lasagne on this page, modify the 'Details' column to create a specification targeted at vegetarians.

Practice examination questions

1 a Why is it necessary for the government to promote guidelines for a healthy diet?

b Explain the term 'balanced diet'.

2 A company is preparing to launch a new pasta salad for school canteens. Labels are required for the foil of the packaging. The specification for the labels is that they must:

- target secondary school children
- be colourful and attractive
- have an Italian theme
- contain the information required by law.

a Use notes and sketches to show two ideas for the design of the pasta salad labels which meet the specification.

b Three of the specification points are given again below. Use these headings to evaluate one of your designs against the initial specification.

- Be colourful and attractive
- Have an Italian theme
- Contain the information required by law.

3 Some products may be irradiated to extend their shelf life.

a Explain the process of irradiation.

b Name three products that could be irradiated to extend their shelf life.

c Irradiation causes concern for some customers. Give three reasons for this.

4 Shelf life is an important consideration for manufacturers of high volume products.

a Give three reasons why shelf life is such an important consideration.

b Describe the correct storage conditions for:

- a fresh chocolate mousse
- a packet of cake mix.

c Packet cake mixes have a long shelf life. Explain two ways in which this is achieved.

5 Food additives have increased and their use has become widespread.

a Name three different additive groups and state their usefulness to food manufacturers and the consumer.

b How has food labelling helped the consumer to make an informed choice?

Section B:

Preparing, processing and finishing materials

Combining and processing 1

Aims

- To understand how food materials may be combined and processed to create more useful properties.
- To understand how combined food materials and **composites** are used to make food products.

When food is processed and combined the resulting food product depends upon the functional properties of the ingredients used. For example, whisking eggs and sugar together traps and holds the air bubbles that make cakes light and well risen. The eggs provide foam and the sugar helps to keep that foam stable. Functional properties are therefore the qualities a food ingredient possesses (both chemical and physical). Combining ingredients may change the functional properties of the original ingredients. Food technologists need to know how ingredients will react when combined with other ingredients.

Once ingredients have been combined they become more complex in structure and further processing is required to shape and form them into various food products. For example, combinations of ingredients may be held together by adding raw egg. When heated, the egg protein coagulates and binds together the other ingredients to form an unbroken shaped product. Therefore, combining an egg with other ingredients (for example, fish and potatoes) will change the properties of the finished food product. The egg will bind the fish and potatoes together to form a fishcake, which will hold together in a better shape than it would without the egg.

Composites

Composites are ingredients or parts of a recipe that have already been processed and come ready prepared. They are used in industry to save preparation time in the manufacturing of food products. Using composites helps to ensure that each product made is of a consistent quality.

Composites are also available in supermarkets for consumers to purchase and use for food production at home. Using composites at home saves preparation time. Examples of composites include:

- ready-made filo pastry
- other ready-made pastries (for example, frozen shortcrust, puff)
- ready-made pastry or meringue cases
- stock cubes
- baking powder
- instant dehydrated foods like soups, sauces and cake mixes.

The ingredients used in fishcakes are combined together to form a new food product with different physical properties to the original ingredients

Examples of the use of composites

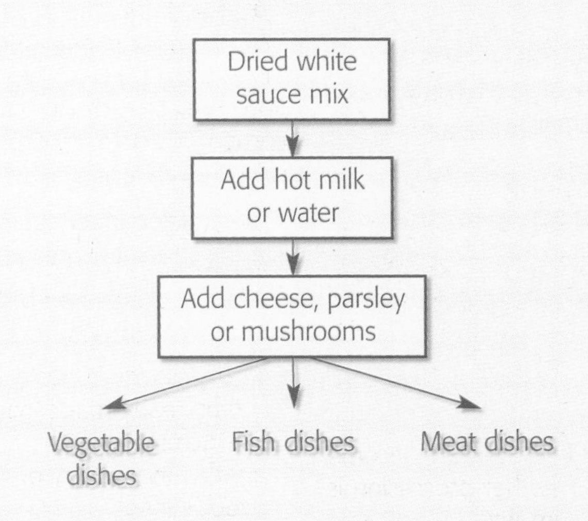

■ Things to do ■

1 Explain the advantages of using composites as an ingredient in the food products above.
Are there any disadvantages?

Combining and processing 2

Aims

- To understand how **secondary processing** can change the shape and size of raw materials to produce more useful properties.

At home or at school you may have used pieces of electrical equipment such as food processors, food mixers and blenders. This equipment saves time and effort during the production of food items. This is mechanical processing on a small scale.

Similar kinds of equipment are used by food manufacturers, but on a much larger scale. In industry, mechanical processing is used to cut, shape, mix, blend and form foods, changing their functional properties in order to create the desired food product. This is called secondary processing (see pages 12-13). Food manufacturers have invested in large and sophisticated (often computerized) pieces of equipment to carry out secondary processing for them.

Mixing and blending

In industry, electrical equipment is used to mix and blend food products. This equipment is labour saving, time saving and economical because large quantities of ingredients can be mixed and blended.

Cutting, shaping and forming

In industry, electrical equipment is also used to cut, slice, mince and grate very large quantities of food materials. The following examples show how large-scale equipment is used in the production of crisps, cheese, pasta, pastry, biscuits and beef burgers.

Crisps

After the potatoes have been washed, they are cut and sliced by mechanical cutters. The cutters are set to the required size and this determines the thickness of the crisps.

Cheese

The addition of rennet to milk results in the separation of the milk into curds and whey (see pages 68-9). In cheese-making large cutters are used to cut the curds into slabs that are turned frequently, to press out the excess whey. The curd slabs are then milled, which means they are cut into smaller pieces called chips. The chips are then pressed into moulds that give the cheese its traditional shape.

Some cheese manufacturers use large electric graters that are capable of grating industrial quantities of cheese. The grated cheese is packaged and used by the food industry as **standard components** in other food products such as pizzas.

A large-scale blender used to blend fruit yoghurt

Pasta comes in various shapes and sizes

Pasta

Pasta dough is kneaded and rolled thinly between large rollers, cut into strips or **extruded** into a variety of shapes.

Beef burgers

Minced meat is used to produce beef burgers. The meat is pushed through electric grinders. For beef burgers, the bore size of the grinder is set very small. This minces the meat finely so that it is suitable for shaping to the required beef burger specification.

Biscuits

Biscuit dough is formed into a variety of shapes using different cutters. Patterns can be imprinted on the biscuit at the same time.

Pastry

Pastry dough, with its elastic properties, can be moulded into different shapes and sizes for use as flan cases, pies, sausage rolls and so on. The **moulding** process used in industry is designed to give a consistent size, shape and weight every time.

Things to do

1. a Design a template for a cutter to shape short-bread biscuits. The **target market group** is the over-60s age group.
   b Design a pattern to be imprinted on top of the biscuit. Create a stamp to imprint your design on to the biscuits.
2. Make up a batch of shortbread.
3. Use your template to cut the dough and your stamp to imprint the pattern on top of the biscuits. Remember that each biscuit must:
   - have the same shape
   - be the same thickness
   - be evenly baked
   - have a uniform pattern imprinted on it.
4. Evaluate your final product and identify any problems you had to overcome. Ask members of the target market group to try your biscuits.
   What did they like about them?

Finishing processes 1

Aims

- To understand that finishing processes are important for aesthetic and functional reasons.
- To understand that finishing processes can change foods so that their **shelf life** is extended and their nutritional value is enhanced.

Finishing processes are used in food production for both aesthetic and functional reasons.

Aesthetic reasons

Food manufacturers will use finishing processes to make food look more attractive and appetizing. These processes enhance the appearance of the product. This is done using a variety of techniques including glazing, icing, piping, colouring and garnishing (see pages 40-1).

Functional reasons

Finishing processes are also important for functional reasons. They can be used to enhance or improve functional properties such as flavour, texture, nutritional value and shelf life. Finishing processes that manufacturers might use for functional reasons include:

- adding flavourings or flavour enhancers to food to replace any taste lost as a result of processing (see pages 16-17)
- using chemical agents such as raising agents or thickeners to enhance a food product's texture (see pages 40-3)
- enriching foods with additional ingredients to enhance their nutritional value (see pages 38-9)
- using preservatives to improve a product's shelf life (see pages 36-7).

The choice of finishing process can change the taste, texture or nutritional value of the finished food product. For example, icing a Christmas cake makes it look more attractive. However, by adding icing, the taste, texture and nutritional value of the whole product has been changed. Therefore, the finishing process has become part of the product identity. It is important to understand that the finishing process used cannot be seen as separate from the product itself. It can change the functional properties of the whole product.

Finishing processes to improve shelf life

In time, all food deteriorates and decays. The rate at which this happens depends upon the type of food and the conditions under which it is kept. Food manufacturers have to ensure that their products remain at their best during production, in storage and until they are consumed. In order to enhance the shelf life of a product a food manufacturer may finish the product by adding fats, oils, sugar, salt and chemical preservatives to everyday foods such as, breads, cakes, biscuits, soups, sauces, jam and so on.

The finishing process has enhanced the properties of this cake

Micro-organisms are the cause of food deterioration. They need food, warmth, moisture and time to multiply. If these conditions are removed then the food is preserved and will have a longer shelf life.

Food can be preserved in several different ways. The finishing process used will depend on the food product.

- Drying removes the moisture that some micro-organisms need to grow – fruit, vegetables, soup, and herbs.
- Freezing and chilling. Moisture is frozen and unavailable to micro-organisms, or the temperature is reduced to a point where they no longer multiply – meat and vegetables.
- Heating. Heat kills micro-organisms, but food must then be sealed in cans or jars – most food can be canned or bottled.
- Chemical. Vinegars, salt, sugar and smoke all contain chemicals that kill micro-organisms – pickled vegetables, smoked meat and fish, jams and chutneys.
- Vacuum packing. This removes air that some micro-organisms need to multiply.

Preservatives

Processed foods such as fruit pie fillings, fruit yoghurts, cheese spreads and soft drinks have a very short shelf life and would soon be unfit to eat if they did not contain preservatives. Manufacturers often use chemical **additives** (see pages 16-17) that help make the food safe for longer.

Adding preservatives in the finishing process is important because they:

- make it possible for food to be available out of season
- help to keep costs of food down because food can be transported in bulk
- make it possible to store food longer at home, therefore reducing the number of shopping trips
- protect food from bacterial contamination.

Finishing processes that enrich foods

Food products can be enriched (improved in quality, flavour or nutritional value) through the addition of other ingredients. Enriching foods includes fortifying them with vitamins and minerals (see pages 10-11) to replace those lost during processing, to improve the nutritional profile of the food or to meet legal requirements. For example:

- manufacturers will fortify dried potato products with vitamin C which is lost during processing
- manufacturers are legally required to add **nutrients** to bread and margarine to protect their nutritional value
- manufacturers may add **fibre, iron** and **vitamins** to products like breakfast cereals so that they can promote them as a more healthy product for consumers.

Eggs, cheese and pulses

Adding ingredients like eggs, cheese and pulses can also enrich food products. These ingredients enrich foods by adding protein and other nutrients. They also improve the colour, flavour and texture of many food products.

Eggs

Eggs can enrich food products like cakes, pastries, pasties, mashed potatoes, custards, sauces, scones and croissants. Eggs will add protein and will thicken dough mixtures because they coagulate when heated. Eggs are also a good source of vitamins B12 and D.

Cheese

Cheese is a preserved form of milk. It is a highly concentrated food with a high fat content. As such, it has a high energy value. It is also an excellent source of protein, calcium and vitamins A and D. Adding cheese to products such as quiche, scones, pizza, croquets and sauces will therefore enhance their nutritional value, as well as their taste and texture.

Pulses

Pulses are the ripened and dried seeds of legumes like lentils, peas and beans. They are a good source of NSP (see page 6). Pulses are a good source of energy, B-group vitamins and, with the exception of Soya (see page 97), of **low biological value** protein. Pulses are cheaper to produce than **high biological value** protein (for example, meat). Manufacturers therefore find them a useful ingredient because they may be used to enhance the protein content of foods cheaply. For example, by adding soya to minced beef or lentils to soup.

Things to do

1 Choose a commercial product.

a Describe the finishing processes used in the manufacture of this product (use the list of ingredients to help you).

b Why do you think these processes have been used?

c Suggest ways in which this food product would be affected if these finishing processes had not been used.

Finishing processes 2

Aims

- To understand that fats, oils and sugars can help in extending shelf life and enhancing nutritional value.

Fats, oils and sugars are sometimes added to food products as a finishing process that will improve shelf life and enhance texture, flavour and nutritional value.

Fats and oils

A wide choice of fats and oils is available and used extensively in food production. They are used because of their physical and working properties.

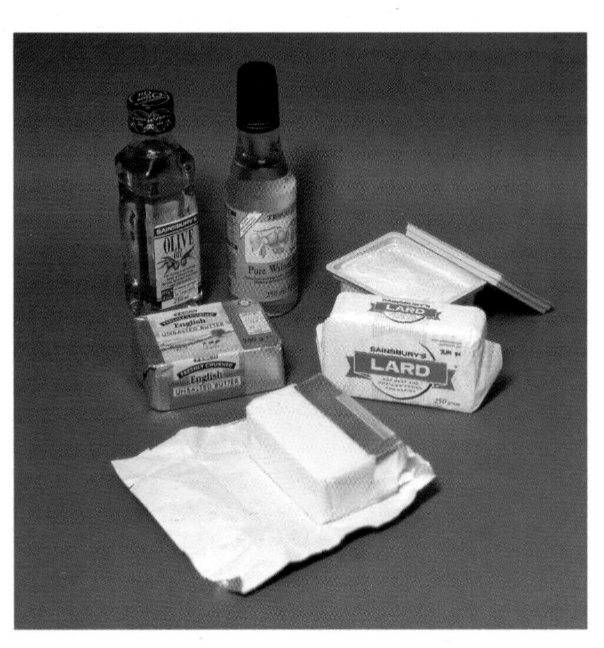

The wide range of fats and oils available

Physical properties of fats and oils

- Fat reacts and melts when heated. The melting point varies for different fats. Overheating can cause fat to burn, discolour and catch fire.
- Fats have a plastic property, when pressure is applied to a solid fat they change shape.
- Fats and oils do not mix with water.

Working properties of fats and oils

- Fats contain vitamins A and D and therefore enhance the nutritive value of food products.
- Fat retains the moisture in baked products (for example, cakes and bread) that prolongs shelf life.
- Fat aerates foods by enfolding and trapping air (for example, in cakes and pastries).
- Fat has excellent shortening properties. It coats flour particles, which prevents the development of gluten (for example, in pastry).
- Fat aids flakiness in pastries and biscuits.
- Fat gives flavour to both fried foods and baked products.
- Fat contributes to the colour of food, for example, roasted meats, fried foods.

Sugar

The wide range of sugars available

Sugar is added to food for a variety of reasons. It is:

- a sweetener
- a preservative
- an energy provider.

Sugar also has physical and working properties. It is used in both sweet and savoury food products.

Caramelized sugar is used as a topping for crème brulée

Physical properties of sugar

- Sugar dissolves in water, especially in hot water.
- Sugar can be heated to a very high temperature. When very hot, sugar melts and liquifies. With continued heat the water evaporates and the sugar begins to change colour. Prolonged heat causes the colour to get darker. This process is called **caramelization**. It is used as a finishing process in food production and acts as a colour and flavour enhancer. However, flavour can be spoilt if sugar is overheated, blackens and burns.

Working properties of sugar

- Sugar sweetens food products.
- Sugar, with fat, helps in the **aeration** of cakes. When sugar and fat are mixed together the air that is beaten into the mixture sticks to the sugar crystals. The fat surrounds the air bubbles and traps them in the mixture.
- Sugar develops colour and flavour in baked sweet and savoury products.
- Sugars attract water and therefore can prevent baked products from drying out, so prolonging their shelf life.
- Sugar may be used as a preservative. Micro-organisms cannot grow in strong sugar solutions. This is why sugar is added as a finishing process to extend the shelf life of fruit, jams and jellies.
- Sugar reduces the development of gluten in cakes and pastries, resulting in a more tender, softer product.
- Sugar contributes to the texture of foods.
- Sugar strengthens the protein in stiffly beaten egg white and helps the mixture retain a large amount of air (for example, in meringues).

Things to do

1. With a partner collect a selection of five different types of fats. Include a low fat spread in your selection.
   a. Spread the different fats on plain crackers. Label each one.
   b. Set up a taste panel and ask the tasters to compare the colour, texture and flavour of each sample. Record the results.
   c. Compare the cost of your selection of fats, energy value per 50g and spreadability at room temperature. Record your results in a table.
   d. Suggest a suitable food product in which each of the selected fats could be used as an ingredient. What properties make the fat suitable for the products you have chosen?
2. Look at the different types of sugar in the photograph on page 38. Identify each one by name and suggest possible uses for each sugar in food production.
3. List six processed foods that contain caramel. Explain the benefits of using caramel in each product.
4. Adapt a recipe for a traditional sponge cake, made by the creaming method, in order to reduce its sugar content.
   a. Make both the traditional sponge cake and the adapted cake.
   b. For each recipe, make a table to record your findings of:
      - ease of creaming
      - differences in shape, volume, texture, taste, colour and cost
   c. Analyse your results.

Finishing processes 3

Aims

- To be aware that physical finishing processes enhance appearance, colour and texture.
- To understand the functions of raising agents and how they are used in the food industry.

Physical finishing processes

Physical processes include:

- glazing (see pages 20-1)
- icing
- colouring (see pages 16-7)
- piping
- garnishing.

Icing

Most cakes can be iced to improve appearance and flavour. Manufacturers use different icings to attract both adults and children to their products. Some of these icings are suitable for piping decorations onto the cakes.

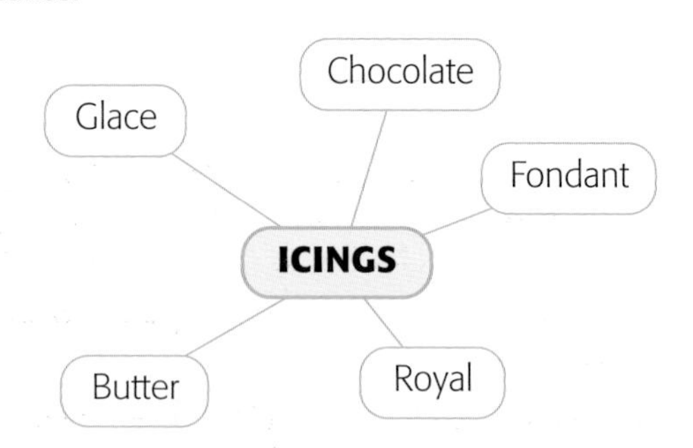

Piping has been used to finish this shepherd's pie

Piping

Some food ingredients may be piped on to food products to enhance their appearance and texture. Piping can be used to create attractive patterns. For example, mashed potato can be piped on to a savoury dish like shepherd's pie. Icing is often piped on to cakes to create lettering, shapes and patterns.

Garnishing

Garnishing is a finishing process used to make savoury products look more attractive. It involves adding a food ingredient to the top of a food product, for example, sprinkling parsley on to a fish pie or putting fresh tomato on a cottage pie. As well as enhancing the appearance and texture of a product, garnishes contribute to the nutritional value of the dish. For example, the tomato on top of a cottage pie is a good source of vitamin A (beta carotene).

Chemical finishing processes

Chemical processes include:

- using raising agents
- using yeasts
- thickening.

Raising agents

Consumers expect products such as bread, cake and pastries to be light in texture and evenly shaped. Raising agents are important in achieving these properties.

This pie has been garnished to improve its appearance and nutritional value

When raising agents are heated a gas is released. This causes the mixture to rise and become light and airy. Raising agents must be harmless, odourless, colourless and tasteless. Raising agents are introduced into a mixture or dough in three ways (see pages 36-7):

- air
- steam or water vapour
- carbon dioxide.

Air

Air is introduced into a mixture by mechanical methods such as sieving, beating, whisking, creaming and folding. All of the methods separate the mixture and allow air to come into contact with more of the mixture. The air is then trapped in the mixture.

Steam or water vapour

Steam or water vapour only acts as a raising agent when there is enough liquid and a high cooking temperature. This allows the liquid to evaporate into steam, which raises the mixture. Products using steam as a raising agent include Yorkshire puddings, Choux and flaky pastries, and cake mixtures.

Steam is the raising agent in this product

Carbon dioxide

Carbon dioxide may be produced biologically from the fermentation of yeast (see page 42). It can also be produced chemically using bicarbonate of soda or baking powder.

Bicarbonate of soda

Bicarbonate of soda (sodium hydrogen carbonate) is produced commercially as a powder. It is used in products like gingerbread and chocolate cake where the strong flavours and dark colour will disguise its unpleasant taste and tendency to darken the crumb. Bicarbonate reacts with a cake mixture when heated to produce carbon dioxide. The CO_2 expands and pushes up the surrounding mixture.

Baking powder

Baking powder is a commercial product made from bicarbonate of soda, cream of tartar (a weak acid) and rice flour or cornflour. The cream of tartar neutralizes the baking powder and removes the unpleasant taste of the bicarbonate. This means it can be used in plain cakes, sponges and scones. Baking powder reacts with the mixture to produce carbon dioxide that causes the mixture to rise.

Things to do

1. Look at the 'Icings' spider diagram on this page. Suggest when you would use each of the icings mentioned. Explain the reasons for your choice.
2. When would you use sieved icing sugar to finish a product?
3. Draw a flow diagram to explain the action of one of the raising agents on this page.
4. Cream of tartar is one acid used to make commercial baking powder. Find out the other type of acids that food manufacturers use and explain why they prefer to use these acids. You could use the Internet in your research.
5. Find out why rice flour or cornflour is added to baking powder.

Finishing processes 4

Aims

- To understand the action of yeast and how sauces are thickened.

Yeast

Yeast is a single-celled micro-organism that grows and reproduces by 'budding'. In order to reproduce, yeast needs sugar, warmth and moisture. As it uses up the sugar, yeast produces carbon dioxide gas. This process is called fermentation.

Yeast is used in the production of bread products and alcohol (see pages 19 and 89). There are three types of yeast available.

- Fresh yeast. This may be blended with warm liquid before adding to flour. A high temperature destroys yeast so care must be taken when using it.
- Dried yeast. This is widely available and has a long shelf life. Providing moisture, sugar and warmth will re-activate the yeast.
- Easy blend yeast. This is fine, very porous yeast that can be added directly to the flour without soaking. Sometimes ascorbic acid (vitamin C) is added to this type of yeast to speed up the fermentation, so that the dough can be made very quickly.

These are two types of yeast available

Thickening sauces

Pouring sauces over, or adding them to a product is a finishing process, used both in the home and in industry. Using sauces changes and enhances the texture, taste and nutritional value of a food product. For example, a white sauce poured over fish gives it a soft texture, makes it more palatable (easier to eat), and adds nutritional value because of the carbohydrates in the flour and the calcium in the milk. Sauces are used in food products to provide the following properties:

- flavour
- moisture
- colour
- nutritional value.

The proportions of the ingredients used and the methods used to make them affect the properties that sauces provide.

Starch-based sauces

Some sauces are thickened to improve their texture and consistency. Starch is added to make them thicker (see pages 16-17) so they are known as starch-based sauces. There are many types of starch-based sauces including white sauce, custard sauce and cook-in sauces.

The following starches can be used to make starch-based sauces:

- cornflour – pure corn starch
- arrowroot – pure starch from a root grown in the West Indies
- wheatflour – a high percentage of starch together with other nutrients (protein, fibre, vitamins and minerals).

When a starch and a liquid are heated together, the mixture begins to thicken. This process is called gelatinization (see pages 17-18). Gelatinization is only complete when boiling point has been reached. There are three different methods of making a starch-based sauce:

- the blended method
- the roux method
- the all-in-one method.

Blended method

The blended method does not use any fat. Blended sauces use cornflour or arrowroot blended with milk or another liquid. This is the simplest sauce and is used for:

- custard – made from custard powder
- blancmange – made from flavoured cornflour, with milk and sugar
- arrowroot glaze – a clear sauce used for fruit flans
- packet sauces (though some may contain fat).

These sauces all use the blended method

Roux method

This sauce is made from equal quantities of fat and flour. The liquid used is either milk, vegetable or fish stock, depending on the sauce being made. The proportion of fat and flour in relation to the amount of liquid is critical because this determines the thickness of the sauce.

There are three types of roux sauce. These have the same amount of liquid but different quantities of flour, which determines the consistency of the sauce. They are shown in the following table.

Type	Amount of flour	Amount of liquid	Use
Pouring sauce	15g	250ml	Serve with vegetables or steam puddings
Coating sauce	25g	250ml	Coating for fish, vegetables and other savoury dishes
Binding sauce	50g	250ml	Used to bind ingredients together, for example, rissoles, croquettes

All-in-one method

This is a very quick method for making a sauce and the ingredients are the same as for a roux sauce (fat, flour and liquid). All the ingredients are put into a saucepan and whisked vigorously during heating to prevent lumps forming. As the sauce boils, the temperature is high enough to make sure that all the starch grains are gelatinized. The sauce will taste fully cooked and be the correct consistency.

■ Things to do ■

1 a Working with a partner, produce two batches of bread using the same basic recipe. In one batch use fresh yeast and in the other batch use dried yeast.

  b Compare the time taken, the appearance, texture and taste of the two batches.

2 a Design a starch-based sauce to be used as part of a vegetarian range of pasta dishes. You may add other ingredients to the sauce to give colour, texture and flavour.

  b Cook the sauce you have designed and freeze half of it.

  c Test the fresh half for appearance, flavour and texture.

  d Defrost and re-heat the frozen sauce. Test it using the same criteria as for the fresh sauce. Compare your results.

  e Analyze the test results and highlight the implications for food technologists of what you have discovered.

3 Using starch is one way of thickening a sauce. Carry out research to find out two other ways of thickening sauces.

Preparation and manufacture 1

Aims

- To understand that nutritional and sensory analysis are used in product manufacture.
- To understand how food manufacturers use nutritional and sensory analysis to adapt recipes to meet **product specifications**.

Nutritional analysis and sensory analysis are two very important techniques used by food manufacturers to ensure their products meet the requirements of the product specifications. Nutritional and sensory analyses are important stages in the preparation of food products for manufacture.

Nutritional analysis

Food manufacturers carry out nutritional analysis for two reasons:

1. to determine if the product meets the nutritional requirements of the product specification
2. to provide information for product labelling.

Meeting the nutritional requirements

The nutritional analysis of a new food product takes place after the recipe has been developed to the product specification. First the product is put through a factory 'trial run'. That is, a batch is made under the same conditions in which the final product will be manufactured. Nutritional analysis takes place after the trial run. A portion-sized piece of the product is tested in the laboratory for its nutritional content.

Nutritional analysis is done at this point to find out if any nutrients have been destroyed during processing (see pages 12-17). If nutrients have been lost then the recipe can be adapted and the food **fortified** (see page 10) in order to maintain the nutritional profile. The manufacturer could add vitamins or minerals and other additives. The manufacturer may also want to make certain claims about the product. For example, they may be designing a low fat product or one that is high in fibre. The manufacturer will carry out nutritional analysis to make sure the product meets MAFF guidelines for low fat or high fibre products (see the MAFF website for these guidelines). If the food product does not meet the guidelines then the recipe will need to be adapted.

Information for labelling

By law, food manufacturers must include some nutritional information on the label of a food product. Nutritional analysis is carried out to determine what nutritional information should appear on the packaging. It is therefore an essential stage of food manufacture.

Sensory analysis

Sensory analysis is carried out at every stage in the development of a food product. It is the scientific measurement of the qualities of a product. Sensory analysis considers the following qualities:

- taste
- texture
- appearance
- smell.

Sensory analysis is essential in the development of food products. This is because the way in which a food tastes, smells and feels in the mouth will determine whether consumers will enjoy eating the product and whether they will buy it again.

Sensory descriptors

Food manufacturers use a taste panel to carry out a variety of tests at different stages of product development. The taste panel might include trained testers and untrained people from the target customer group or from different sections of society.

As everyone's sense of taste is slightly different, the taste panel will need to agree on the meaning of words used to describe the taste, texture, appearance and smell of a product. The words used are called **sensory descriptors**. For example, the taste of a product might be described as burnt, herby, sickly, spicy, stale, fragrant or fishy. Everyone on the taste panel would need to agree what is meant by these terms before using them to describe the product.

Quality	Some sensory descriptors
Taste	floury, salty, bitter, sour, sweet, tangy
Texture	dry, brittle, soggy, tough, moist, crunchy
Appearance	dull, greasy, bright, attractive, stale, fresh
Smell	burnt, spicy, fragrant, herby, fishy, cheesy

Carrying out sensory analysis

In industry, sensory analysis tests take place in a test kitchen or booth, which must be:

- hygienic
- well lit
- free from smells.

The food samples are randomly labelled and are equal in size and quantity. Tasters are given clear instructions and record their results on tables/charts or enter them directly into a computer. Various methods of recording the results are used in industry (see pages 46-7).

If the results from the same product are unsatisfactory (for example, if the panel decides that the product does not meet the requirements of the specification), the product will be modified. A new taste team will analyze and evaluate the modified product and this will continue until a satisfactory result is achieved.

Using the results

The results from sensory analysis enable manufacturers to:

- adapt new product recipes at each stage of development to ensure they meet the requirements of the specification
- modify existing products. For example, to make a lower fat version or a cheaper version that retains the sensory qualities of the original product.

■ Things to do ■

1. Explain the importance of nutritional and sensory analysis in preparing a product for manufacture.
2. Nutritional analysis on a new healthy pasta salad for children showed that the product was too high in fat. What steps could be taken to modify the recipe so that it contained less fat?
3. Carry out a taste test on a mint (for example, a Polo) by following the steps below.
   a. Hold your nose tightly so that you have to breathe through your mouth. Place the mint on your tongue and then chew it very hard. Make a note of the taste.
   b. Release your nose and make a note of the taste.
   c. Compare the two tests and state the difference in taste.
4. Try the same test with an eating apple and record your results.

A taste panel testing a food product

Preparation and manufacture 2

Aims

- To understand the different types of sensory tests.
- To be aware of how food manufacturers use sensory analysis to meet product specifications and to prepare food products for manufacture.

Sensory tests

On pages 44-5 we saw how food manufacturers use sensory analysis during the development of a food product. There are a variety of sensory tests that are used to carry out this analysis. The type of test used depends on what the manufacturer wants to find out. The different types of tests can be divided into:

- Difference tests – these are comparative tests between different food samples.
- Ranking tests – these sort food samples into an order of preference or in order of a particular sensory characteristic (for example, chewiness).
- Rating tests – these are used to find out how much the taster likes or dislikes the different samples.
- Star profiles – these are used so the taster can describe the **sensory characteristics** of a food sample.

Difference tests

Difference tests are used when a change of ingredient or process has been made (perhaps as a result of earlier testing), or for comparison with a competitor's product. The types of difference test used include:

- paired comparison tests – where the taste panel tests two samples of the same food in order to find out if there is any difference between them in relation to a specific attribute. For example, this test might be used to compare the moistness of the manufacturer's fruitcake with that of a competitor.
- duo-trio tests – use three samples, two of which are identical. The taste panel is told which is the control (one of the identical samples) and is asked to say which of the other two samples is different from the control. Again, this might be used to find out if the manufacturer's product is similar to that of a competitor. This test might also be used to see if an adapted recipe (for example, a lower fat version) has similar sensory characteristics to the original product.
- triangle tests – similar to the duo-trio in that it uses three samples, two of which are identical. However, in this test the tasters are not told which is the control. They are asked to pick the sample that is different from the other two. This is a useful test when the difference between products is very small. Again, this test would be used if the manufacturer wanted to develop a product similar to one already on the market, or wanted to modify an existing recipe but retain the same sensory characteristics.

Triangle Test

Name: ....

Two of the samples are the same. Tick the odd one out.

X531

X315

X135

Ranking tests

In ranking tests, the taste panel is asked to put the samples in order of preference. The tasters could be asked to rank the samples according to the strength of a particular sensory characteristic (for example, how sweet is it?). Symbols are usually used for each sample so that the taster is not influenced by product names.

Ranking Test

Name: ....

Taste the samples and put them in order – the chewiest first and the least chewy last.

Samples	1	2	3	4	Comments
♣					
♦					
♥					
♠					

Rating tests

Rating tests are designed to find out how much the tester likes or dislikes a product. A rating test with a descriptor is used to find out how much the tasters like a particular sensory characteristic or characteristics of the product. The scale used in this test is called a hedonic scale.

You can use a pictorial or verbal hedonic scale. This is an example of a five-point verbal scale.

1 dislike a lot
2 dislike a little
3 neither like or dislike
4 like a little
5 like a lot.

An example of a five-point pictorial scale

Rating score	1 ☺	2 ☺	3 😐	4 ☹	5 ☹
Sample A					
Sample B					
Sample C					

This is an example of a rating test with a descriptor asking about particular sensory characteristics of a product.

Tasting words	Votes by Tasting Panel					Total	Av'ge
Chewy	3	2	1	2	3	11	2.2
Moist	3	2	3	1	1	10	2
Nutty	2	2	1	2	1	8	1.6
Fruity	3	1	1	2	1	8	1.6

Star profiles

Star profiles are diagrams used to describe the exact taste, texture and appearance of food products. Several sensory characteristics can be compared at the same time and the results can be used to write a **product profile**.

To produce a **star diagram**, a star shape is drawn with each line marked 0 to 5. Each line is labelled with a word that describes the product, for example, soft, bitter and so on. The words used will depend on the product being tested. The food is tested and the results are plotted on the star diagram. The marks are then joined together. This gives a detailed 'at a glance' profile of the product being tested. Star diagrams can be drawn by hand or with a computer.

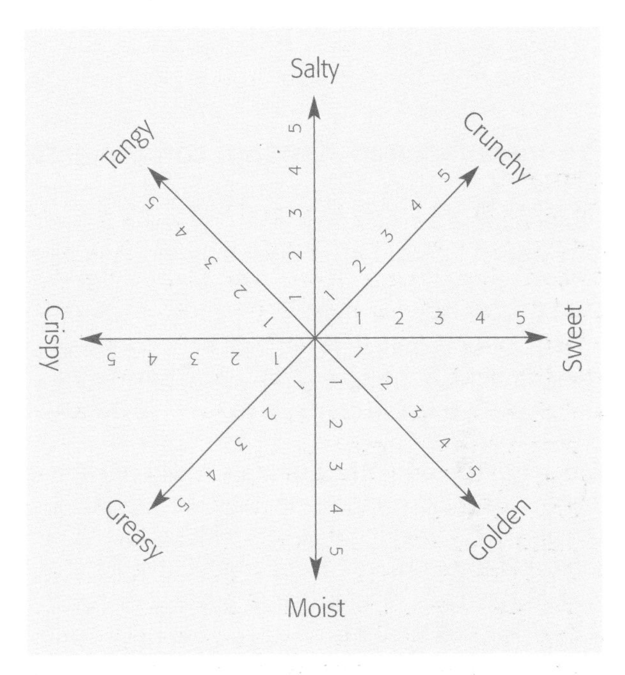

■ Things to do ■

1. List all the reasons why manufacturers use so many different tests when adapting recipes to meet specifications.
2. With a partner, organize a taste panel to see if people can tell the difference between a low fat crisp and an ordinary crisp. Use one of the three difference tests explained on this page.
3. Choose five sensory descriptors that could be used to describe a cereal bar and create a star diagram using these descriptors. Test two or three different cereal bars and plot your results on the star diagram. Use a different colour for each cereal bar.

   Using the results, try to write a description of each cereal bar.

Preparation and manufacture 3

Aims

- To understand how pre-manufactured standard components are used to produce consistent food products.

Pre-manufactured standard components

In the food industry pre-manufactured standard components are ready prepared, processed ingredients that are 'bought in' and used by the manufacturer to produce other, more complex food products. Therefore, instead of making a food product from scratch using raw ingredients, many of the components of a food product will have been made by other, specialist food manufacturers.

The specialist food manufacturers must guarantee that the standard components they produce always contain the same ingredients, which have been subjected to the same processing techniques. This enables the food manufacturer to produce consistent and reliable final products.

Why use standard components?

Food manufacturers use standard components for a number of reasons. These include:

- It is more cost-effective to use standard components than it is to invest in the machinery and trained staff needed to assemble food products from raw ingredients.
- Standard components are quick and easy to use, saving both time and money. They are also quick and cheap to make in large quantities.
- Using ready-prepared standard components means that a manufacturer will have fewer health and safety issues to deal with. For example, using a pre-manufactured pizza base means that the manufacturer has to handle fewer raw ingredients like eggs, which can easily become contaminated.
- Standard components help to ensure that the products made are of a consistent quality. For example, using pre-manufactured flan cases helps to ensure that all the flans made are the same shape and size.

Examples of standard components

- Pre-blended herbs and spices
- Stock cubes
- Mixed fruit
- Fruit pie fillings
- Pasta shapes
- Grated cheese
- Cooking fats

Some uses of standard components

Some standard components can be used to make a variety of different products. Some of these uses are outlined in the charts below:

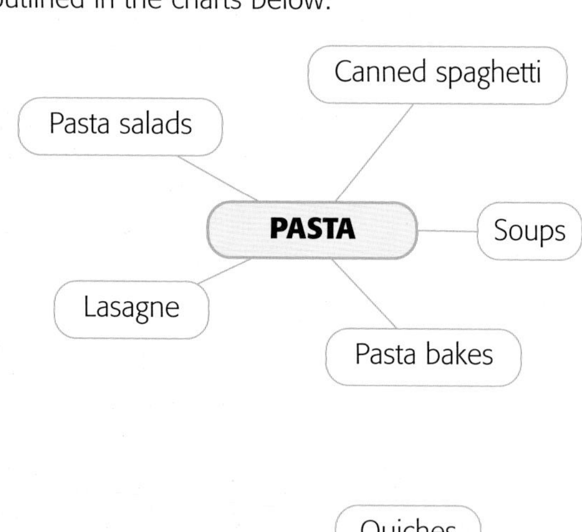

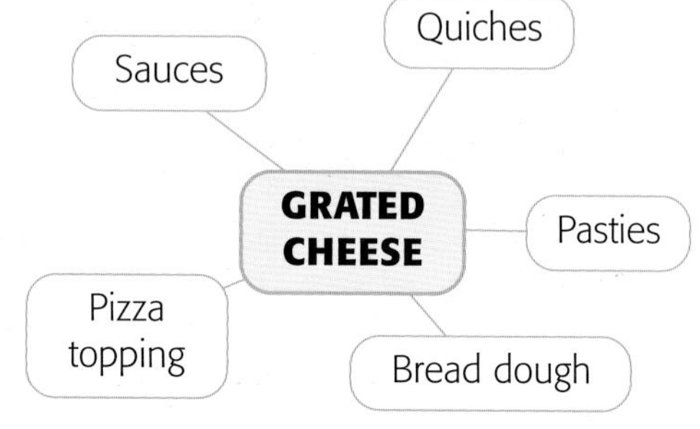

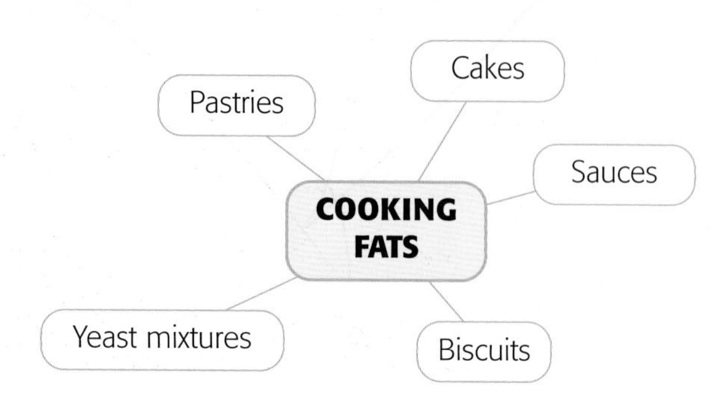

Other standard components have a more specific use. For example, pizza bases and flan cases are only used to make pizzas and flans.

Food manufacturers also buy pre-mixes, such as pre-blended spices and mixed fruit, as standard components. These save time because the manufacturer does not have to blend all the individual spices or fruits themselves.

Unit operations

Before any raw ingredient can be used as part of a standard component, primary processes (see page 12) are carried out. These processes are called unit operations. Each ingredient is a unit of a finished food product so unit operations are the primary preparation processes carried out on individual ingredients.

Cleaning, peeling, sorting and washing are the kind of unit operations used to process raw ingredients like fruit and vegetables. Cleaning and peeling the potatoes used for crisps, or washing lettuce in chlorinated water for use in sandwich fillings, are examples of unit operations.

Mincemeat is one unit of mince pies (the other being the pastry cases). It is often bought as a standard component. Unit operations such as cleaning, sorting, peeling and chopping will have been carried out on the ingredients before they are sold to a manufacturer for use in mince pies. Because of the amount of equipment and expertise required for **primary processing**, it is easy to see why mince pie manufacturers buy mincemeat fillings for pies as standard components.

Quality control

As with all food products, the quality of standard components is checked very carefully at all stages of manufacture. Quality is checked frequently to make sure the products meet specification requirements and that they are of a consistent quality.

■ Things to do ■

Standard components are used in the home as well as in industry.

1. a. Choose a standard component, such as a pre-manufactured pizza base, and cook as instructed.
   b. Make the same product using raw ingredients.
   c. Do a comparative test of the home-made product and the standard component. Use sensory descriptors appropriate to the product you have chosen. Also note down the time each product took to prepare.
   d. If time allows, repeat steps a–c so that you can compare the consistency of your products.
   e. Evaluate your results and use them to outline the advantages and disadvantages of using standard components.
2. Why do you think it is important to food manufacturers that food products are of a consistent quality?
   How do pre-manufactured standard components contribute to the consistent quality of the overall product?

Pre-prepared standard components in mince pie manufacture

Quality of manufacture

Aims

- To understand the importance of accurate weighing and measuring to ensure quality of manufacture.
- To understand how materials are cut, shaped and formed to achieve specified **tolerances**.
- To understand how to scale up recipes for small and large **batch production**.

Quality

A quality product is one that is 'fit for its purpose'. It fulfils all the requirements of the product specification. (see pages 49 and 66 for more on quality).

Quality assurance

Quality assurance is the assurance given by the manufacturer that its products meet certain standards. The manufacturer guarantees that the product:

- is safe to eat, the correct weight and meets it's nutritional and advertising claims.
- meets any legal requirements.
- **quality control** has been employed during manufacture.
- is the same product that the consumer bought the last time.

In order for a manufacturer to be successful it has to convince its customers that its products are consistently of a high standard. If customers have confidence in a manufacturer they will continue to buy its products and may try other products produced by that company. Quality assurance is about improving, maintaining and promoting a quality food product.

A computerized weighing machine

Weighing and measuring

When manufacturing products of a consistent quality, it is vital to weigh and measure ingredients accurately. In industry, large-scale computer-operated machinery is used to make sure each item or portion produced is exactly the same size, shape, and includes exactly the same quantity of ingredients, as all the others.

Quality control systems (see pages 74-7) are used in industry to ensure a consistent result. When manufacturing a food product in large quantities computer-controlled machinery is used to weigh and measure ingredients and products accurately (see the biscuit-making example below).

Biscuit making

- Dry ingredients are weighed using a computerized weighing machine.
- Accurate proportions of ingredients are combined in a mechanical blender to form the biscuit dough.
- The dough is either passed through two cutters that cuts and shapes the biscuits to exactly the same size, or the dough is **extruded** into a standard shape and cut up with a wire cutter.
- The biscuits are put on a conveyor belt, which travels through a computer-controlled oven. The oven has different heat zones. The biscuits pass through the hot zone and then into a cooler zone until the cooking is complete.

It is possible to produce consistent results at home or in the classroom. There is a range of small-scale equipment to help you to weigh and measure accurately. For example, electronic scales can help you to weigh ingredients accurately to the required weight every time.

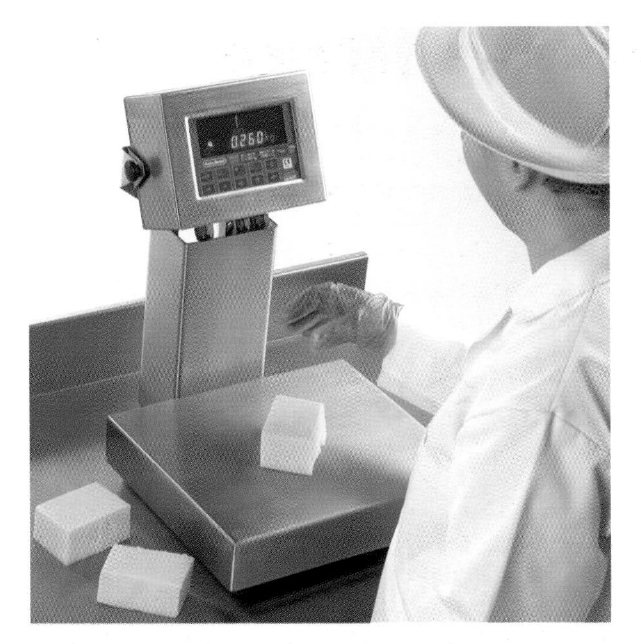

Electronic scales

Measuring spoons

You can also use measuring spoons to ensure a consistent quantity of ingredients in every batch.

Tolerance levels

Even with the most sophisticated equipment it would be difficult to get every batch of a product completely identical. Therefore, every product specification will allow for a slight variation in the desired weight, temperature, colour and size. This variation is known as the tolerance level and it is shown by a plus (+) or minus (–) amount either side of the target value. If the ingredient quantity or product weight is within the tolerance level then the manufacturers know that the finished product will be of the required quality and will retain the required sensory characteristics.

For example, the specified tolerance for the size of chopped onions in a Cumberland pie is 10mm ± (plus or minus) 1mm. This means that although the target size is 10mm, the onions can be 9mm or 11mm without reducing the quality of the finished product.

If the tolerance level *is* exceeded in either direction (too much or too little) then the product would be rejected. The consistency of quality and sensory characteristics of the product could no longer be assured.

Scaling up recipes for small and large batch production

Most food manufacturers have test kitchens where small-scale recipes are made. After testing and trialling to ensure the product meets the desired specification, the recipe can be scaled up for batch production. This means that the amount of each ingredient is increased but the proportion of each ingredient stays the same. In order to make sure that the proportions are the same, the manufacturer will calculate the percentage of each ingredient in the original recipe.

Things to do

1 a Accurate weighing is crucial to the success of the final product. To test this, make up the following bun recipe to produce six buns. This will be the control batch.

- 50g caster sugar
- 50g margarine
- 1 medium egg
- 50g self-raising flour

b Add another 25g caster sugar to this recipe and make another six buns.

c Assess the shape, taste and texture of both batches. Produce a chart to record your results. Analyze your results and highlight the differences between the two batches.

d Using your results as evidence, explain the importance of accurate weighing.

What impact would inaccurate weighing have on a manufacturer?

e Scale up the bun recipe for a batch of 60 buns. Compare the cost of making six, as opposed to 60 buns, and then calculate the cost of each bun in a batch of 6 and a batch of 60.

Health and safety 1

Aims

- To understand the importance of the safe use of materials, components, tools, equipment and processes.
- To recognize a hazard and to know when hazards might occur in the food production process.

Food safety

By law commercial food products must be safe to eat. Food poisoning **bacteria** can very easily contaminate food. These bacteria can infect food materials, tools and equipment. Manufacturers must ensure they comply with health and safety regulations and prevent food contamination at any stage of the production process.

Legally, food manufacturers have to train all food handlers in health and safety requirements. Food handlers must understand why protective clothing and personal hygiene are necessary, and they must comply with the law.

Causes of food contamination

Food poisoning can easily happen as food poisoning bacteria can infect food from a wide range of sources. These can include the following:

- Dirty equipment and tools.
- No pest control.
- Food areas dirty and unhygienic.
- Incorrect food storage.
- Foreign objects coming into contact with food (for example, jewellery).
- Poor personal hygiene habits.
- Disinfectants used for cleaning equipment.
- Incorrect food preparation.
- Inaccurate timings (for example, for cooking and chilling).
- Incorrect temperatures for cooking/refrigeration/ serving.
- Poor standards of serving foods.

High-risk foods

High-risk foods are those that are more likely to contain food poisoning bacteria. Meat, fish, cream, eggs and soft cheeses should be stored at temperatures of 8°C or below to reduce the risk of bacteria multiplying (as bacteria need warmth to multiply).

On arrival at the food factory all foods are checked for quality and to make sure they are free from contamination. If accepted by quality control the high-risk foods are stored in refrigerators at 5°C. Frozen foods are stored in freezers at below −18°C. Refrigerators and freezers are checked regularly to make sure they are at the correct temperature. Separate refrigerators must be used for different foods to avoid cross contamination. For example, raw food is stored separately from cooked food.

	Some health and safety laws	
Law	**Description**	**Reason**
Food Safety Act 1990	It is an offence to sell any food that is harmful to health, contaminated, falsely labelled or advertised.	To help to reduce the number of cases of food poisoning.
Food Safety (General Hygiene Regulations) 1995	Lays down standards for premises, equipment and personal hygiene. Covers the preparation, processing, manufacturing, distribution, handling and selling of food products. Anyone involved in these must set up **systems** to avoid food contamination and be able to prove they have shown **due diligence**. Covers hazard analysis, risk assessment and food hygiene training.	To ensure the safety of food.
Food Safety (Temperature Regulations) 1995	High risk, perishable foods must be kept below 8°C. Hot food must be kept at a temperature above 63°C.	To avoid food contamination.

The safe use of tools and equipment

Health and safety also involves the safe handling and use of tools and equipment. Potentially dangerous equipment is also used in the home and classroom. For example, sharp knives, mixer blades, mandolins, electrical equipment, gas cookers, cleaning fluids and deep fat fryers are all tools and equipment that are potentially harmful unless they are used safely. It is very important to understand how to use tools correctly and to follow the correct procedure when operating equipment.

Industrial food manufacture involves the use of complex and sometimes dangerous machinery. All working environments should have written safety procedures covering things like what to do in case of fire, conduct in the work place and instructions in case of accidents. Employers are required by law to provide a safe working environment for their employees. The relevant laws are:

- Health and Safety at Work Act
- RIDDOR – Reporting of Injuries, Diseases and Dangerous Occurrences Regulations
- COSHH – Control of Substances Hazardous to Health.

All surfaces and equipment that come into contact with food must be easy to clean and regularly disinfected. In industry, equipment and tools are thoroughly cleaned and sterilized after each production run to prevent contamination. In a continuous flow production plant, where machinery is running all the time during the week, it is switched off for three hours over the weekend for deep cleaning.

Premises also need to be free from infestation from pests such as rats, cockroaches, fleas and so on. The manufacturer must have a pest control policy in place to ensure the cleanliness of the buildings.

Hazards

In food production anything that may cause harm to the consumer is called a hazard. There are three kinds of hazard:

- physical, for example, mice droppings, metal or glass in food.
- biological, for example, bacteria, moulds and yeast. All these micro-organisms can contaminate food, which then becomes unfit to eat. For example, salmonella in chicken and raw eggs, mould on bread and yeasts causing yoghurt to ferment.
- chemical, for example, disinfectants and cleaning agents used in cleaning equipment, which could contaminate food.

These hazards could occur at any time during the production process.

Process	Hazards that could occur
Harvesting raw ingredients	Chemical contamination through overuse of pesticides. The presence of harmful bacteria, moulds or foreign bodies.
Primary processing of raw ingredients	Contamination by micro-organisms, pests or chemicals. **Cross-contamination** of different components.
Transportation of ingredients to manufacture	Bacterial contamination due to unclean lorry or food being transported at the wrong temperature.
Secondary processing of ingredients	Cross-contamination or bacterial growth. Contamination by food handlers, foreign bodies, incorrect temperatures, dirty equipment.
Storage	Incorrect temperatures allowing micro-organisms to grow. Storing past the use by date.

Things to do

1. Write out a set of instructions for the safe storage of a high-risk food such as fresh mince.
2. Twenty-four hours after eating a cold buffet at a wedding reception, half of the guests were taken ill. Suggest how and why this might have happened.
3. List the precautions that should be taken to prevent cross-contamination between raw and cooked foods.

Health and safety 2

Aims

- To understand how risks are assessed.
- To understand how **HACCP** is used in the food industry.
- To understand the need for an effective control system to ensure food safety.

Risk assessment

In order to reduce hazards, food manufacturers have to identify levels of risk at each stage of production. This means identifying:

- the risk of a hazard occurring
- the seriousness of the risk in terms of the consequences of the hazard (for example, the risk of food poisoning)
- ways of preventing, reducing or eliminating the hazard.

This analysis is known as risk assessment. The main method of assessing risk is through use of the HACCP (Hazard Analysis of Critical Control Points) system.

HACCP

HACCP is a food safety system designed to identify and reduce the risk of hazards occurring throughout all stages of food production – from harvesting of raw materials to storage at the point of sale.

Food handlers must wear protective clothing to prevent contamination

A control point is the point at which a hazard could occur. A **critical control point (CCP)** is a point at which action *must* be taken to reduce or eliminate the risk of food contamination. Food manufacturers must have a HACCP system in place to ensure the safety of their food products. HACCP is a quality assurance system because, by using HACCP, manufacturers can assure consumers that their products are safe. However, they must also ensure that anyone handling food understands the need for safe and hygienic practices.

Low- and high-risk areas

The production areas in a food manufacturing plant are divided into low- and **high-risk areas**. **Low-risk areas** are where the food ingredients are handled before being processed. The ingredients are cleaned and then passed into a high-risk area.

The high-risk area is also known as the clean area. This is where the food ingredients are processed and packaged to make the finished product. Once food has passed into the high-risk area it is never sent back into the low-risk area to avoid the risk of **cross-contamination**.

Food handlers

Food handlers will work in either the low-risk area or the high-risk area (but never both) to avoid the risk of contamination. Handlers are also prevented from handling both raw and cooked food, as this could cause microbial contamination. Protective Personal Clothing (PPC) must be worn by food handlers to protect the food from human contamination. PPC includes:

- hairnets
- hats
- clean overalls
- clean aprons
- plastic gloves
- plastic overshoes.

Things to do

1 The table below describes the HACCP process for a meat sandwich. Choose a different food product containing a high-risk ingredient. Create a table to show the HACCP process for your food product.

A section of a HACCP process for a meat sandwich

Step	Hazard (controls)	Preventative measures – what can I do about it?	Monitoring – how can I check?	Corrective action – what if it's not right?
Defrosting of frozen ingredients	* Bacterial growth if temperatures rise above 5°C. * Physical, chemical and bacterial contamination to product or by product to other foods.	* Defrost in a refrigerator and store below 5°C. * Clean refrigerators. * Store raw ingredients below cooked ingredients. * Cover mixture during storage.	* Check and record refrigerator temperature daily. * Check food for smell and colour. * Check date codes.	* Adjust or repair faulty refrigerators. * Keep raw/cooked foods separated. * Discard out of date foods.
Preparation	* Growth of bacteria if held too long at room temperature. * Physical, chemical and bacterial contamination to product.	* Prepare quickly in a cool area, ideally a 10°C room. * Ensure that the products are kept at **ambient temperature** for the minimum time. * Ensure all surfaces and equipment are clean and disinfected. * Ensure good personal hygiene. * Check for foreign material potential, for example, glass.	* Ensure preparation takes place within 90 minutes and finished products are returned to refrigeration. * Carry out cleaning checks. * Check on staff hygiene practices. * Ensure sanitizer is available and used.	* Train staff in procedures. * Ensure supervisors are aware of risks. * Carry out spot checks. * Carry out regular checks for foreign material items. * Discard any product if out of chiller for too long or contaminated.
Holding and display (CCP)	* Physical, chemical and bacterial contamination.	* If product is displayed at ambient temperature, the period must not exceed 4 hours and preferably for two hours. * If held below 5°C and either wrapped or covered, store for maximum of 48 hours. * If on open display, whether chilled or not, discard after each service. * Ensure all sandwiches are date coded with production and use by dates.	* Carry out regular date coding checks. * Check temperatures are taken and recorded. * Ensure good personal hygiene. * Ensure adequate supplies of sanitizer available and used. * Check that food is not exposed to risk of contamination.	* If temperatures rise above 5°C during storage discard after 4 hours. * Ensure staff is aware of temperature and time limits. * Give training on stock rotation if required. * Record food wastages on wastage sheet/book.

Source: British Meat Education Service

Health and safety 3

Aims

- To identify where hazards might occur.
- To understand that checks are made at critical points in food production.

In the manufacture of these burgers, several critical control points have been checked to ensure a safe and good quality product

Critical control points

The points in the production process at which hazards have been identified must be monitored and controlled to ensure a safe production operation. Points where hazards may occur are known as **critical control points (CCP)**. Specific checks are carried out at each control point and data is collected and recorded, either by a computer system or manually by a trained operative. The flowchart below and the table opposite show how this is applied in the production of beef burgers.

Summary of critical control points for meat for beef burgers

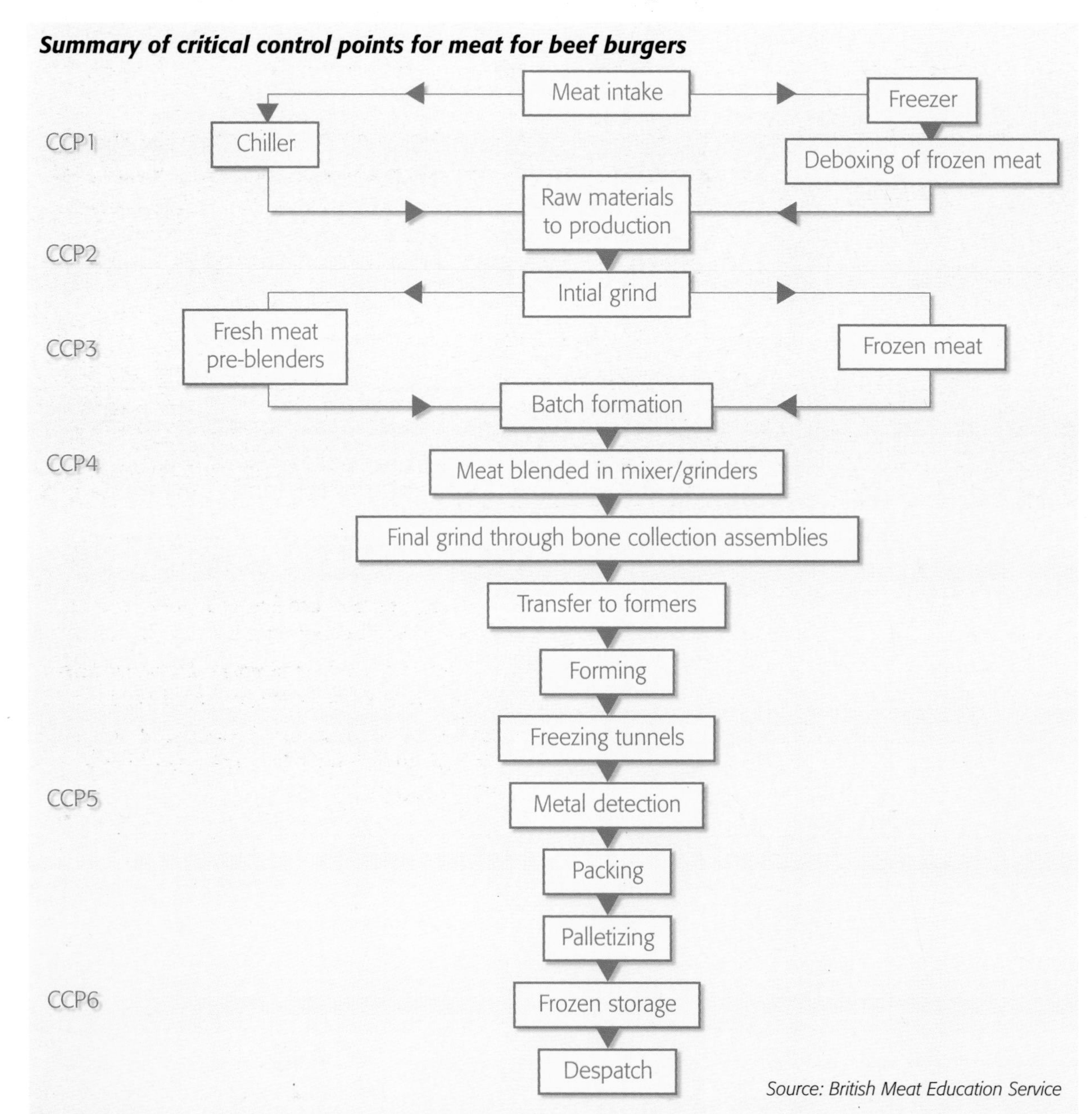

Source: British Meat Education Service

Summary of critical control points

CCP	Critical limits
CCP1. Meat intake	• Meat must be from a current audited and approved supplier. • All vehicles must be sealed on delivery. • Vehicles must be clean, without off-odours, fit- for-purpose and free of other materials. • Fresh meat temperature: target < +4 °C. • Frozen meat temperature: target < –18 °C. • Fresh meat less than six days from kill date. • Packaging fully protects meat against possible contamination risks. • Meat is bright red colour, no off-odours, free of any slime or contamination.
CCP2. Raw material storage	• Chiller temperature operating between 0°C to +5°C.
CCP3. Frozen meat storage	• Freezer temperature operating between –15°C to –25°C.
CCP4. Defect eliminators	• Defect eliminators fitted to all final grinding heads to remove bone and gristle fragments.
CCP5. Metal detection	• In-line metal detectors fitted with automatic rejection systems at freezing tunnel exits. • Detector sensitivity set at 1.2mm ferrous (metal containing iron), 1.5mm non-ferrous (metal not containing iron).
CCP6. Product storage	• Product kept at < –18°C.
CCP7. Factory hygiene	• Daily strip-down and clean of all manufacturing equipment. • Foam detergent followed by sanitizer. • Daily visual inspection. • Microbiological swabbing.

■ Things to do ■

1. a. Design a production flow chart for a product you have made recently.
   b. Identify where hazards may occur and indicate the critical control points on your flow chart.
2. Explain the importance of the four points listed in Critical Control Point 7 'Factory Hygiene' in the table opposite.

Using ICT and CAD in single item production

Aims

- To understand how ICT, including Computer Aided Design (**CAD**), is used to generate, model and communicate design proposals in single item production.

Information and Communication Technology (ICT), including the use of CAD/**CAM**, is increasingly being used by the food industry to develop and manufacture products. This section identifies those stages in the design process where ICT might be used to help generate, model and communicate design proposals for the manufacture of a one-off product. ICT could be used in the following design stages:

- identifying needs
- developing detailed specifications
- developing product ideas from the specification
- modifying product ideas to meet the specification
- communicating product ideas
- producing detailed work schedules.

Identifying needs

- Research into products already on the market can be done using the Internet. For example, you could visit the websites of major supermarkets like Tesco, Sainsbury's or Iceland. The Internet can also be useful for researching the latest food issues, for example, the Food Standards Agency website.
- Questionnaires are a well-tried method of researching the needs of the target market. If you have access to a spreadsheet you can input research information, analyse it and display the results in the form of graphs, pie charts and diagrams.
- Some clip art packages provide images suitable for use on image boards, food labels or packaging.

Developing detailed specifications

- Specifications can be drawn up using a word processor. They can be stored on disk and opened as and when modifications to the specification are required.
- CD ROMs, like those produced by British Nutrition Foundation, and the Internet (for example, www.nutrition.org.uk), include up-to-date nutritional information. They can help you:
  a decide on the nutritional requirements of your target market
  b to modify recipes to meet the specification
  c to analyse products.
  Some CD ROMs and websites include databases of recipes that can be helpful when designing new products.

Developing product ideas

- CAD programmes can help with the design of new product ideas. New shapes, patterns and colours can be tried on screen before a prototype product is made.

A selection of food-related clip art images

Digital images and CAD packages can help when modifying designs

- A spreadsheet package could be used to cost out design ideas.
- Design ideas could be modelled using a food-modelling programme. You input the ingredients and the programme will model the final product for you. This will demonstrate the final outcome without having to actually make the product. This programme can also be used to modify a food product by changing the ingredients themselves or by altering the relative proportions of ingredients used.

Modifying product ideas

- One way to evaluate product ideas is to test them using a taste panel. The results can be input into a spreadsheet programme that can easily convert them into charts. These provide an at-a-glance analysis of the taste panel's view of a product. Modifications can then be made to the product in order to match the target market's requirements more closely.
- Digital cameras could be used to take digital images of the original and modified product. The images could then be imported into a CAD package and text added. This would provide a useful visual record of the modifications that have been made, and the text would record the reason for the modifications. Alternatively, a digital image of the original product could be altered in a CAD package to show the effect of changing the colour or shape of the product.

Communicating product ideas

- Digital cameras, word-processing packages, spreadsheets and presentation packages (for example, PowerPoint) can all be used effectively to communicate your ideas for new food products.
- E-mail is a useful tool if you need to send your design ideas to potential consumers, to manufacturers for advice or to other students if you are doing project work.

Producing detailed work schedules

- Before a product is manufactured, flow charts detailing work schedules need to be produced. These need to highlight the critical control points in your process. In order to identify potential hazards you could use software that models the growth of bacteria (see page 13).
- Using spreadsheets is an easy way of **scaling up** recipes for batch production (see page 28).

Things to do

1. a. Design a cook chill pasta-based dish suitable for a vegetarian.
   b. Using nutritional analysis software, work out the nutritional content of the product.
   c. Design a flow chart for the production of your pasta dish. Indicate the hazards and critical control points throughout the process (see pages 56-7).
   d. Use a spreadsheet to cost your product.
   e. Further work could include setting up a taste panel, designing a questionnaire, analysing the results using a spreadsheet and recording the information in the form of a graph.

Using ICT, including CAM, in single item production

Aims

- To understand how ICT, including CAM, is used in single item production.

As well as being useful in the design process, ICT can be useful in the manufacture of food products. CAM can be helpful in the production of a quality product in school or at home.

CAM is the use of computer-controlled machinery to manufacture products. CAM is widely used in the food industry and most of the processing and production machinery is monitored and controlled by computers. This ensures a consistent product and, to some extent, reduces the need for a large trained workforce.

In the home and school environment smaller scale, computer-controlled equipment is now used on a regular basis. This can be used to simulate large-scale industrial CAM production. This machinery includes:

- microwave ovens
- timers
- bread ovens.

Used in one-off production, this equipment can have benefits similar to those of the larger CAM equipment used in industry. They can:

- save time
- help ensure a consistent result
- help ensure the production of a good quality product.

Microwave ovens

Microwave ovens are examples of CAM because many have computerized programming facilities. In one-off production, the oven can be programmed to cook the product at a certain temperature and for a specific length of time.

The advantage of using a microwave oven is the speed and ease of defrosting, cooking and reheating. Different settings for different types of food have been programmed into the microwave during manufacture. This allows for more accurate cooking temperatures and time control than with a conventional oven.

Microwave ovens are constantly being updated with new features and innovations. One new innovative feature is 'Inverter Technology'. The advantage of this feature is that the ovens are more powerful, which means faster cooking and reheating. Inverter Technology maintains a constant power that provides even cooking and reheats food more efficiently with no hot or cold spots.

Features of some microwave ovens include:

- Computerized touch-screen pads. These are designed for ease of use – simply touch the pad to operate the microwave oven and read the instructions from the screen.
- Weight sensor. The sensor weighs the food and the programme calculates the cooking time required.
- A variety of cooking modes and programmes. For example, defrosting frozen food, cooking vegetables, meat, chicken, pastry and cakes.

The popularity of cook chill convenience foods has led to the design of a new microwave oven. This oven automatically reheats the meal of your choice. Enter the weight of the meal as marked on the package and the oven will reheat your chosen meal to the correct temperature.

The latest microwave technology

Timers

Computerized timers are widely used in industry. They help to ensure that each processing stage in food production is exactly the same length of time, every time. This is vital if the manufacturer is to achieve a consistent result.

On a smaller scale, in the classroom, computerized timers can be used to measure time accurately. These timers are built into equipment such as microwaves and breadmakers, but are also available separately. For example, digital timers could be used for the accurate timing of each stage in the production of a one-off product.

A digital timer

Bread makers

Bread makers are a good example of small-scale use of CAM to produce a consistently good product in a short amount of time. They show how computer-controlled machinery does all the work that would traditionally take up a lot of time if done by hand.

The latest models also use automatic programmes so that bread can be made at any time of the day. All the ingredients can be added the night before. The digital timer can be pre-set up to thirteen hours ahead of time. The machine kneads, proves, shapes and bakes the bread over night so that fresh bread is ready in time for breakfast. There is a touch control panel that makes for simple programming. On some appliances there are thirteen automatic programmes, and on one appliance there is a jam making facility as well!

CAM technology in the home

Things to do

1. List the advantages and disadvantages of using CAM in one-off production. Are these the same advantages and disadvantages as using CAM in industry? Give reasons for your answer.
2. Investigate how ICT is used for product development in industry (use pages 58-9 to help you). Create a chart that compares the industrial uses of ICT with those available to you at school.
3. List the stages in the design and making process for a new food product. At the side of the page, write in the ways in which ICT could help you develop your ideas effectively. Are there any stages where ICT would not help you?

Practice examination questions

1 a Large electric graters are used in food manufacture. Name two different foods these graters could be used for.

b Name the piece of electrical equipment found in the home, which can be used for grating food.

c Many manufacturers buy in ready grated foods as a standard component part.

i Explain what is meant by a 'standard component part'.

ii Describe two advantages to a food manufacturer of using standard component parts.

2 a Identify four critical control points in the production of roast beef sandwiches.

b Describe the cleaning process of the production line after the roast beef sandwich run.

c Explain why the cleaning process of the production line is essential after each product run.

3 Describe the outcome for a sponge cake mix if too much of the following were added:

- caster sugar
- margarine.

4 Explain the importance of accurate weighing of ingredients when mass-producing sponge cakes for large retail outlets.

Section C:
Manufacturing commercial products

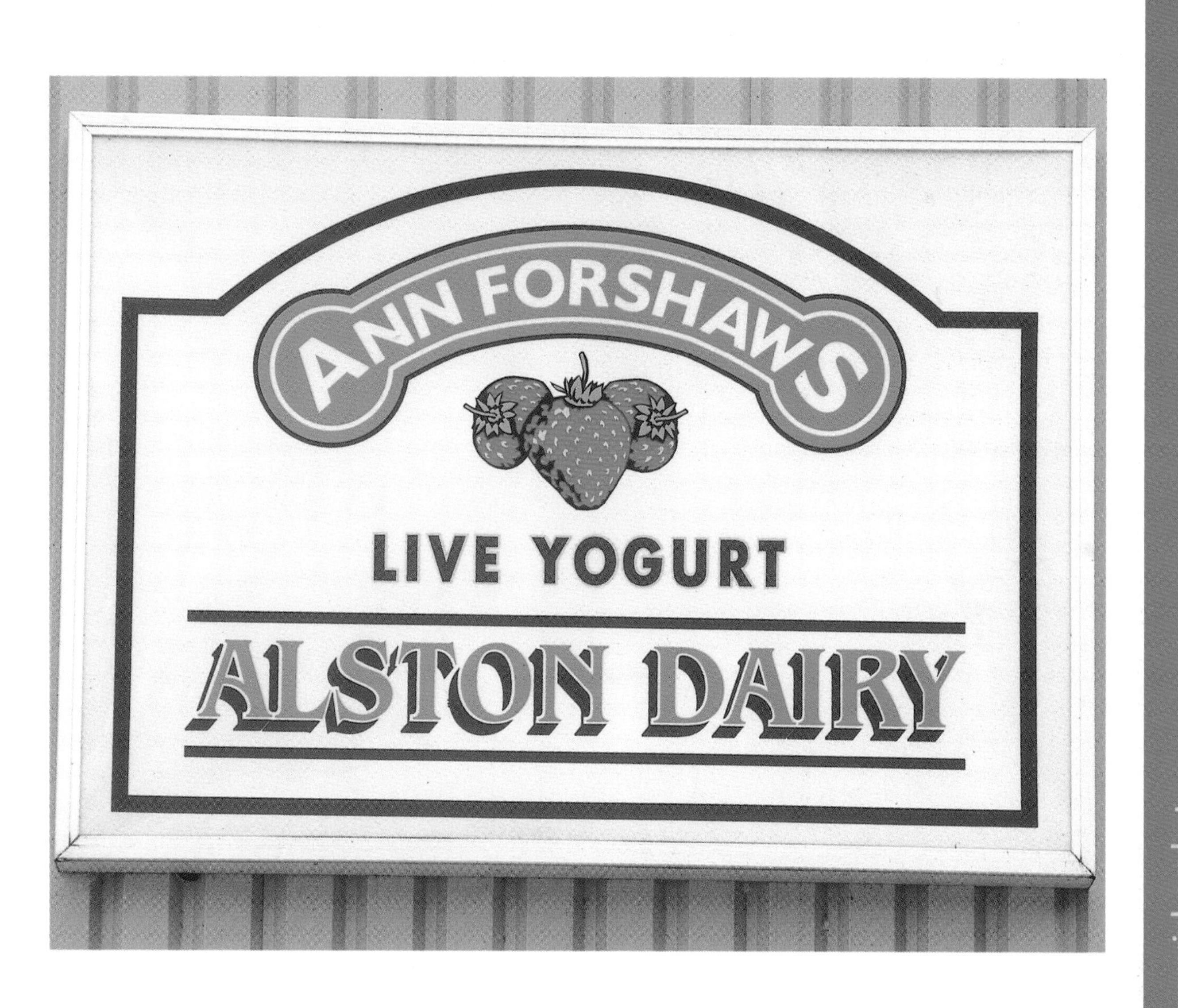

Manufacturing commercial products

Aims

- To understand the manufacture of single products and products in quantity.

Product manufacture

The **target market group**, and the **product specification** for that market, determines the scale of production. These factors will determine the size of the manufacturing plant required and the machinery within it.

Food manufacturing plants can range from small factories, such as a local bakery, to very large factories, such as Heinz Canned Foods or Warburtons Bread. Small food manufacturing plants make products in fixed batch sizes, often only a few dozen in a batch. Large-scale manufacturers may produce several thousand items in one batch (for example, in pasta production), or a continuous flow of products (as in the manufacture of crisps).

'One-off' production (or jobbing)

This is the name given to the production of individual, often hand-made items. Celebration cakes are a good example. Highly skilled craftspeople design and make these specialized cakes to individual customer specifications. These items take hours to make, one person makes each cake, they may use unusual and expensive ingredients, and the cakes therefore often have a high price.

A handmade celebration cake

Batch production

This process is used when a fixed number of products are required. This process will involve the use of specialized equipment and the different stages in the process are combined in a production line.

In **batch production** many of the machines have interchangeable parts so that other similar products may be produced on the same production line. For example, pasta machines can have different dies (cutters) to change the shape of pasta. This means that production can be switched from one batch of pasta to another, depending on when the orders need to be fulfilled. All machinery on the production line is cleaned between each production run.

The cost of batch production is more economical than 'one off' production because greater volumes of ingredients are required and these can be bought more cheaply in bulk. Also, automation may mean that fewer, less skilled staff is required.

Sterilizing equipment after a production run of yoghurt

Crisp production at Snack House

The production of crisps at Snack House is a good example of continuous flow production. Because crisps and snack foods are in high demand and usually have a long shelf life, the production line at Snack House runs for 24 hours a day, seven days a week. The production line stops only if there is a mechanical fault or some equipment needs repairing or cleaning. Because this process is fully automated and computer controlled the work force is very small.

Potatoes used for crisps at Snack House are grown to the company's specification. They are continually being transported from the grower to the factory.

The potatoes are tipped into hoppers that allow the potatoes to fall onto a conveyor belt. The grids on the conveyor belt determine the size of potatoes used. The specification requires that the potatoes be of a certain size in order to be suitable for crisp production. The grids allow potatoes that are too small to pass through. As the potatoes move along a conveyor belt they are also checked for shape and colour.

The potatoes are then sliced within covered slicing machines and are moved along the line to be blanched. There are small viewing windows placed near each process so that operatives can check the **system**.

After blanching, the sliced potatoes are moved along and fried at the same time. Frying temperatures are monitored very carefully at this stage to maintain crisp quality.

The crisps then fall down a chute to a large holding tray where they are visually checked for blemishes. The crisps then move up a chute to a drum that flavours the crisps.

The crisps then enter the packaging stage. They are dropped from the flavouring drums into a bag and sealed. The bags are weighed as they pass along the system before being packed into boxes.

The product is then stored ready for transportation to retail outlets.

Continuous flow

This is a continuous process that uses highly efficient machinery. This machinery is kept running without stopping unless there is a break down, a problem with a product or cleaning is required. Identical products are produced continuously 24 hours a day, seven days a week. The aim is to achieve a high level of **output** and consistency every day. This process is suitable for bread and some food products with long **shelf life** such as breakfast cereals and crisps.

The equipment is automated and computer controlled. This cuts down on the labour force and labour costs. Operatives check on the correct working order of the machinery and, because they do not touch any of the foods, they do not require food-handling skills.

Things to do

1 Visit your local supermarket and cost their range of celebration cakes. Record the list of ingredients and the weight of each cake.
   - a Sketch one of the cakes and identify the target market for this cake.
   - b Compare the cost of the supermarket celebration cake with a similar one at a local bakery.

2
   - a Identify six different pasta shapes on sale in your local supermarket. Record the price and ingredients of each type at the same weight.
   - b Some pasta shapes are more expensive than others. Give your reasons for why this might be.

3 Visit the supermarket and find out the price of a large sliced white loaf made by a large bread manufacturer. Compare the price of this loaf with the same sized loaf made by the supermarket's in-house bakery and one made by a local bread shop. Taste each one and evaluate the results. Is there any relationship between price, quality, taste and texture?

Record your results in a table.

Case Study 1
Alston Dairy Ltd Yoghurt

Alston Dairy Ltd

Alston Dairy Ltd in Longridge, Lancashire, produces yoghurt for sale in the farm shop, other retail outlets and supermarkets. The company started on a small scale in the farmhouse kitchen, using the excess milk from the day's milk yield.

Food safety procedures

The yoghurt is now made on a commercial scale in premises that have been extended to meet the demands of yoghurt production and of the food safety regulations. A very strict code of hygiene is applied and all operatives are trained in the **HACCP** system (see page 54). All operatives wear protective clothing including hairnets, hats, gloves and wellington boots. Outdoor clothes are stored in different coloured lockers from the clean work clothes.

A small wall divides the **low-risk area** from the **high-risk area** of production (see pages 54-5). Operatives crossing the wall from the low-risk to the high-risk area have to wash their hands and sterilize their wellingtons in the boot scrub.

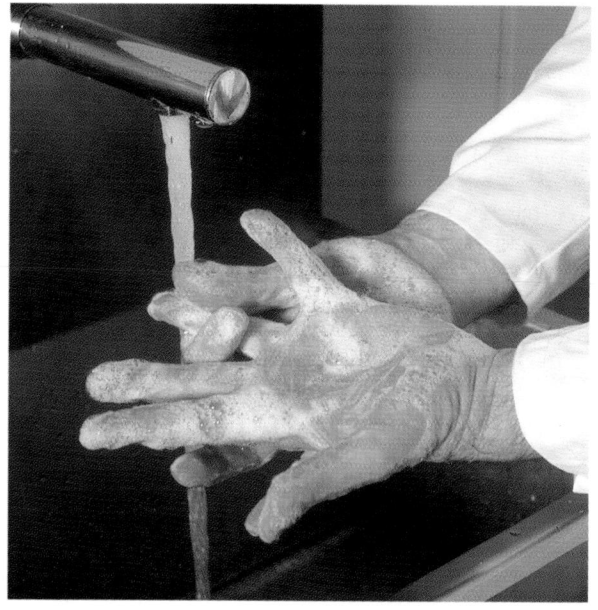

Hand washing is required before entering the high-risk area

Once in the high-risk area, operatives and food must not return to the low-risk area. All these safety procedures ensure a quality and safe product.

Careful records are kept for each batch of yoghurt produced. In the event of a safety hazard, these records help to trace where the problem started and the necessary action can be taken. See the HACCP flow chart on page 56.

Product specification

A product specification is used for every batch of yoghurt produced. This gives a precise description of all the ingredients, including weight and the method of mixing.

Quality checks

All incoming deliveries of raw materials and other goods to the diary are checked to ensure that:

- they are free from foreign bodies
- they are of the correct specification
- the packaging is undamaged
- there are no 'off' odours and foods are within their shelf life
- the temperature is correct.

The temperature for chilled products must be 0–5°C and for frozen products the minimum temperature of −18°C.

The cleanliness of each delivery lorry is checked on arrival at the dairy. Goods will only be accepted if the safety procedures are met. Records are kept on the date of delivery, the supplier's name, the vehicle registration number, as well as on the safety checks made on incoming raw materials.

The lorries collecting the yoghurt for dispatch to the retail outlets are also checked for cleanliness and the correct storage temperature.

Yoghurt production

The milk used during production depends on the type of yoghurt being made. Whole milk or skimmed milk can be used. Whole milk gives a creamier taste because it contains more fat. Yoghurt made from skimmed milk can either be low fat (containing less than 1.5% fat) or fat free (containing less than 0.5% fat).

The milk used at this dairy is from the farm's own herd. The milk is pasteurized on the premises. Skimmed milk and dried skimmed milk powder, used for the organic range of yoghurts, is bought in.

Yoghurt culture

Milk is turned into yoghurt using **bacteria** called *Baccillus lactus*. These are added to the milk as a **bacterial culture**. The bacteria grow and produce lactic acid that thickens the milk and creates the acidic flavour of yoghurt. The culture arrives at the diary freeze-dried and is stored at –43°C.

The pasteurized farm milk is pumped from the dairy into large vats. The culture is added to the milk, which is gently heated to 43°C. At this temperature the bacteria coagulates (clots) the proteins in the milk causing it to thicken.

The clotting of the milk takes about $2\frac{1}{2}$–3 hours in a carefully controlled environment. This is called the incubation period.

The yoghurt is then cooked to 5°C and stored at that temperature. The bacteria are still active at this temperature and the yoghurt becomes slowly more acidic. This is natural yoghurt with no other flavourings added. Natural yoghurt can be potted and packaged at this stage.

Flavoured yoghurt

Altson Dairy uses whole fruit to flavour their yoghurts. After the incubation period a quantity of a specific whole fruit is stirred into the yoghurt. This is done using a large mechanical blender because it blends the mixtures evenly.

The blending machine

After blending, the fruit yoghurt is transferred into smaller vats for use on the production line. The yoghurt is pumped from the smaller vats into plastic yoghurt pots and sealed, all in one operation.

The filled pots are fed onto the conveyor belt and placed into trays. They then move along the production line into the area where each pot is passed through the metal detector before being shrink-wrapped.

The trays of yoghurt are then stored on palettes and moved to the cold store before being dispatched to the retail outlets. After each product run of specific fruit yoghurt all the equipment and machinery is swabbed down and sterilized.

■ Things to do ■

1. Conduct a survey of the different types of yoghurt available in the supermarket.

   Identify the target market for each one.
2. Record the amount of fat per 50g for six different types of yoghurt.
3. Compare the costs of the six different yoghurts you have chosen.
4. Set up a taste panel to taste the six different types of yoghurt. Record the results.
5. Create a table that compares the type of yoghurt, amount of fat, cost and taste. What are your conclusions?

Case Study 2
Singleton's Dairy

Singleton's Dairy

Singleton's Dairy began making cheese in a farmhouse kitchen in 1934. Today they produce over 2,500 tons of cheese every year, for a wide variety of markets (bulk, pre-packed and deli-counter). The dairy is a good example of large batch production.

The cheeses produced are dispatched into Europe on a daily basis and to North America every week.

From milk to cheese

Cheese is a concentrated form of milk and is a good example of **secondary processing**. When milk is stored past its shelf life it turns sour. This is because lactic acid-producing bacteria are in abundance. If the storage temperature is suitable for their growth they will convert the lactose (milk sugar found in cream) into lactic acid. This curdles the milk and forms solid clots and liquid. This is called curds and whey. This clotting process is the basis of cheese production.

Lancashire cheese production

Raw milk is delivered to the dairy and stored in large vats.

To destroy harmful bacteria, the milk is heated to a temperature of 71.7°C for fifteen seconds and then rapidly cooled to 10°C. This process is known as **pasteurization**.

Storage vats

After pasteurization, the milk is pumped into large open tanks and a starter culture of lactic acid bacteria is added. This is used to sour the milk. The temperature is raised to 30°C.

A technician checks the level of bacterial activity and when sufficient lactic acid has been produced vegetarian rennet is added to clot the milk and produce curds and whey. Vegetarian rennet comes from an **enzyme** called chymosin that is derived from vegetable sources. All the cheeses produced at Singleton's are suitable for vegetarians.

After 45 minutes the mixture is cut with special knives that helps to separate the curds and whey.

The separation of curds and whey

The curds and whey are then heated to 40°C, which also helps to shrink and separate the curds. This is called scalding. Temperature control is critical. This is because the **micro-organisms**, which help with the next stage of the process, will be destroyed if the temperature is too high.

The whey is allowed to drain away from the curd. This whey is used in another process to help make cream and butter. The curds are cut into large slabs that are laid on top of each other. The pressure allows further whey to drain away. Salt is then added to preserve and flavour the cheese.

An electrically driven curd mill cuts the curd slabs into smaller pieces called 'chips'. The chips are put into lined metal moulds, covered with a metal lid and the moulds are then placed in long rows, end to end, and put under great pressure. This removes more whey and shapes the cheese.

The pressed cheeses are knocked out the next day and bound in cheesecloth. The cheeses are pressed again and allowed to dry before waxing and vacuum sealing.

Cheese drying

The cheeses pass through a metal detector and are then stored in a temperature-controlled storeroom where they are allowed to mature before dispatched to retail outlets.

■ Things to do ■

1 Find out the differences between the manufacture of hard cheeses and soft cheeses.

2 a List four hard cheeses and four soft cheeses. Identify the fat content per 25g of each cheese.

  b Set up a panel to compare the taste, texture and appearance of each cheese. Decide on a five-point measurement system that you will use to record the panel's responses. Design a chart to record all the results. Summarize your conclusions.

3 Suggest ways of using the favourite cheese in a food product.

Case Study 3
Sandersons Confectioners

Sandersons is a family run bakery producing a wide variety of baked products for their own confectioner shops and other retail outlets. Sandersons produce 600 loaves and 4000 bread rolls every day. The bread products range from white loaves and rolls, to wholemeal and granary loaves and rolls. The bakery also produces savoury pies and pasties, iced fancy cakes, sausage rolls, sponge cakes and fresh cream cakes.

The processes used in the bakery are semi-automatic (for example, some processes are operated by hand and some by machine). The work force needs the skills necessary to work on a variety of different processes. Some ovens are computer controlled and the programme is able to adjust the oven temperature and length of cooking time to suit the different products.

Sandersons Bakery produce 600 loaves every day using computerized oven timers

Savoury pies

When making savoury pies, a weighed amount of pastry is placed into each foil tray by hand. The trays are then placed on a blocking machine that rotates and moulds the pastry base. The filling is then added from a hopper above and a rolled out pastry lid is placed on top as the blocking machine rotates. The pastry lid is pressed and crimped into shape. This seals the pie. The pies are then placed on large baking trays ready for the oven.

Sausage roll production

The sausage roll making machine is computer controlled. The puff pastry is rolled to the required thickness and placed in a cutter at the beginning of the manufacturing process.

The pastry passes underneath two cutters. The first cutter cuts the pastry into strips and the second cutter makes the slashes that are traditional on the top of a sausage roll. The pastry is brushed with water.

Piping the sausagemeat

The sausage meat is held in the hoppers and fed through pipes onto the moving strips of pastry.
As the pastry and the sausage meat move through the machine, it passes through metal channels. These turn the pastry and produce long lengths of sausage roll. The long sausage rolls are then cut to the required length and pass onto baking sheets ready to be baked in the ovens.

Hand finishing

The work force at Sandersons are all highly skilled and hand finish many of the products made at the bakery, such as piping cream into éclairs and spreading glacé icing onto vanilla slices.

Finishing the sausage rolls

■ Things to do ■

1. As a team, develop a specification for different flavoured sausage rolls. You may use ready-prepared puff pastry. Draw a **flow chart** indicating the CCPs (critical control points – see pages 56-7) for the production of sausage rolls.
2. Form a production team to produce the new sausage rolls. Each team member must have a specific job to do.
3. Use a spreadsheet to calculate the cost of each sausage roll. Estimate the labour costs.

   Work out the profit you would make if you sold them to a food retailer.
4. Using a graphics/DTP package, design suitable packaging for the sausage rolls.

   Design the label.

Case study 4
Inter Link Foods plc

Inter Link Foods plc produce a wide variety of cakes and tarts at their many bakeries throughout the UK. They produce cakes for major high street supermarkets.

One of the major lines is Cherry Bakewell Tarts. Inter Link produce 16,000 every day. The plant used is semi-automated. This means they have both computer-controlled equipment and a work force that carries out the tasks that the mechanical equipment cannot cope with. For example, it is much quicker and easier to apply the cherries by hand because they are sticky and could cause a hazard with the machinery.

Making the tarts

The pastry mix ingredients are weighed and put into the mixer by hand. It takes just 40 seconds to mix the pastry mechanically. The pastry is then placed into a hopper above a conveyor belt and measured amounts of the pastry dough are dropped into each foil case below. Weight sensors and cutters ensure the correct amount of pastry is being put into each foil case.

Pastry is dropped into the foil cases

The pastry in the foil cases travels to the blocking machine (see Case study 3). This moulds the pastry before it moves along the conveyor belt to the jam dispenser. After travelling through the jam dispenser, the tarts pass along the conveyor belt to the sponge dispenser. This dispenses the correct amount of sponge mix into each tart.

The pastry is moulded into the cases

The tarts are passed on to baking trays and move into the travelling oven for sixteen minutes. After baking, the tarts are allowed to cool for two hours.

The cooled tarts are passed to the icing machine and the correct amount of icing is piped on to each tart. Cherries are placed on top of the tarts by hand.

The Bakewell Tarts are finished by hand

A box of tarts passing through a metal detector

The tarts are then placed into preformed trays before being conveyed to the cling wrap machine. Finally, the boxes pass through a metal detector and are automatically placed into cardboard boxes for dispatch.

Things to do

1 You have been asked by a manufacturer of Bakewell Tarts to design a filling and topping for a new range of sweet tarts for children. The filling is contained in a pastry case.

   a Design a new filling and topping for the tarts.

   b Using exploded diagrams, sketch three design ideas and add notes to explain your ideas. Carry out research to help you decide which design you will carry forward.

   c What do the filling and topping ingredients add to the final product in terms of nutrition?

   d Draw up a manufacturing specification and a flow chart for making six tarts of the final design.

   e Make the tarts.

   f Compare your product with other tart products on the market. Evaluate cost, taste and texture.

   g Record your evaluation using a spreadsheet.

Case study 5

Warburtons bakery was established in 1870. It is a leading independent bakery group producing ten million loaves of bread a week. Warburtons uses very sophisticated computer integrated manufacture (**CIM**) systems.

Stages in bread production

At Warburtons every stage of the production process is computer controlled. This includes:

- measuring temperature and liquids
- weighing individual ingredients and the formed dough
- mixing the dough
- dividing the dough into pieces
- kneading and shaping the dough
- proving the dough
- **moulding** the dough pieces
- baking times
- de-panning
- cooling
- slicing
- packaging.

All ingredients are checked against the bread specification by the baker's own laboratory. The ingredients are transferred from large storage containers into the dough mixers automatically. Dough is mixed in batches of 300 kilos for about three minutes in a carefully controlled temperature of 28°C.

The mixed dough being dropped into tins

When mixing is complete, the large mass of dough is tipped into a divider. This cuts the batch of dough into pieces suitable for 400g or 800g loaves. The pieces of dough are passed into a conical moulder, kneaded and shaped into balls.

The dough pieces are allowed to 'recover' for about six–eight minutes as they travel around the conveyor. This is called the first prove. After proving, the dough is moulded into shape and dropped into the tins. It then travels along the conveyor belt to the prover where the temperature and humidity are carefully controlled.

Dough is deposited in pockets in the prover

The dough is left to prove for about 50 minutes. Then it is passed into the travelling oven for baking. The gas-fired ovens have two temperature zones and each zone is carefully monitored. The first zone is much cooler than the second zone, which has a higher temperature of 200°C. The bread is baked for twenty minutes.

Some specialty breads, such as 'soft white', undergo another process before baking. They move from the prover to a piece of equipment that slashes the top of the loaf with a very powerful jet of water. This creates the characteristic split on top of some loaves. Then the loaves pass under the flour dispenser. The flour is dispensed from metal sifter trays with wire mesh templates. The sifter trays are computer controlled and are shaken pneumatically.

Loaves being passed under the flour dispenser after being slashed with a water jet

After baking, the loaves are de-panned. This piece of equipment gently lifts the loaves out of the baking tins using rubber suction cups, which are operated by a pneumatic control system. The loaves are placed on to a conveyor system and are passed into the cooler. Here a computer carefully controls temperature and humidity. This process lasts about $2\frac{1}{2}$ hours. It enables the bread to be sliced easily and is also done because the bread must not be packed warm. After cooling the bread is sliced and packed by either bagging or wrapping in waxed paper.

During the manufacturing process a loaf of bread is weighed every ten minutes as part of the **quality control system**. The bread is automatically grouped into batches of fifteen, using position sensors. The loaves are passed through metal detectors and automatically fed onto the loaf trays, which are stacked before being transported to the delivery vans.

■ Things to do ■

There are a wide variety of different flavoured breads available in the supermarkets (for example, cheese and onion, sun-dried tomato and so on).

1 a In a group, conduct a survey of the different varieties of flavoured bread available in your local supermarket. Make a list of the breads, and the cost and weight of each one.

b Buy four different kinds of flavoured bread and set up a taste panel to compare taste, flavour, texture, shape, size and cost. Record your results.

2 a With a partner, design a new flavoured bread for a supermarket. Design the product for large batch production. Design the product for the summer picnic market.

b Using the information on bread production, produce a flow chart for the production of your bread in high volume. How will you ensure consistency?

c Produce an annotated sketch of your bread and indicate the function of each ingredient.

d Make a batch of the bread.

e Set up a taste test for your class. Decide which taste test you would like to use to obtain realistic results about your bread.

f Using a spreadsheet analyze the results of the taste test to display to the rest of your class.

3 Collect a range of different bread labels and compare the nutritional content of a slice of each bread.

Case study 6
Park Cake Bakery

Park Cake Bakery in Oldham is the largest single site supplier to a major high street store. This plant supplies over 200 different products and launches 140 new lines each year. They also produce 90,000 custard tarts every day.

Pastry cases for custard tarts

Mixing equipment

Some very highly sophisticated mixing equipment is used in this food plant. One mixer is used for making choux pastry and is computer controlled with an integrated heat sensor and temperature control. The same mixer can also be used for heating and mixing custard sauces for puddings and Manchester tarts.

Fruit pie assembly

Not all the equipment at Park Cakes is computer controlled or able to undertake some of the processes of food production. Therefore, some of the tasks are done by hand. One example is the assembly line for fruit pies where **components** are placed into the mould by hand.

After the fruit filling has been added by machine, the pie is fed into the nitrogen tunnel by hand for immediate freezing. Liquid nitrogen, which is extremely cold, is sprayed on to the food in the tunnel. After leaving the nitrogen tunnel a jelly topping is applied by machine. The operatives, who wear protective gloves, pass the pies along the line to the final process. Here the pies are boxed and stored in large freezers.

Fruit pies entering the nitrogen tunnel

Operatives moving the pies along the assembly line

Quality control

Quality control is a major feature on all the production lines. Samples of every item, from the raw ingredients to the final product, are checked for quality every ten minutes and each sample is recorded.

Equipment like the metal detectors is also checked for performance and possible mal-function. For example, ferrous (metal) and non-ferrous (non-metal) probes are inserted into sample products before they are conveyed through the metal detector to see if it is working.

Laboratory checks

Samples of products are checked in the laboratory for contamination by bacteria such as Salmonella and E-Coli. Samples of cake are also tested for moisture content.

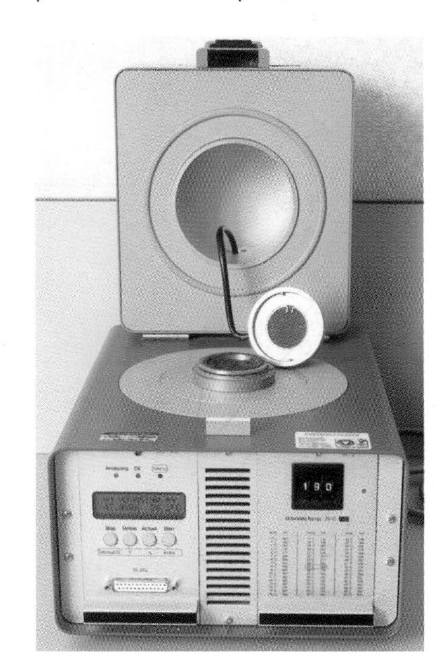

Machine for testing the moisture content

1 a Investigate the popularity of frozen desserts with your class. Make a list of the most popular deserts.

b Cut open a frozen desert to see how it has been assembled. Sketch the cross section of the desert and label it to show how it is constructed.

2 a Design a new frozen desert suitable for a child who is a diabetic. The dessert must also be nutritionally healthy to attract the parent (for example, the person actually buying the product).

b Design a label for the desert giving clear instructions for storage and defrosting.

The use of ICT and CAD/CAM in batch and volume production

Aims

- To show how computers are used in food manufacture.
- To show an understanding of the use of **CAD/CAM** in batch and volume production.

Advantages of a computer system

An effective computer system can contribute to the food manufacturing process in a number of ways:

- Provides efficiency in the process and systems, and for the workforce.
- Enables a faster product time to market.
- Reduces waste.
- Can save money by lowering costs.
- Provides information and **feedback**.
- Monitors quality.
- Enables the production of consistent and high quality products.

The use of computers in a food manufacturing plant

Computers can be used at every stage of the food design and production process. As the diagram above shows, computers may be used to:

- carry out market research and analysis
- improve communications, both internally (within the organization) and externally (with suppliers and customers)
- design new products using computer aided design (CAD) software
- order and purchase raw materials
- collect and analyze data about raw ingredients entering the food plant using databases
- process the final product using computer aided manufacturing systems (CAM)
- streamline and integrate all aspects of the production process using computer integrated manufacture (CIM)
- invoice suppliers and retailers.

The uses of ICT in food manufacture

Using computers for effective communication and information management in the food industry

Databases

Every detail about a product can be stored in a database. This will include information about raw materials, pre-manufactured components, recipes, specifications, costings, quality control data and so on. Details of the date and time of delivery of ingredients, their sources and visual check records are stored on a database. As a result, if a problem arises, the source can be identified and the problem solved immediately. A database also enables everyone in the production team to have access to information about the products.

Electronic data interchange (EDI)

Orders come in to a food manufacturer from a distribution centre through electronic data interchange (EDI). This computerized system provides up-to-date information about the orders. These can change for many reasons. For example, the season of the year can dictate the demand for a particular product. Promotional activity with a food outlet can have an impact on the expected sales for a product. Therefore, up-to-date sales information allows the manufacturer to work out the quantity of products required, and the quantities of the raw materials needed to make them.

Using computers for communication

Computer systems are essential to food manufacturers because they are an efficient and effective means of communication. Electronic data links such as E-mail and the Internet makes the exchange and gathering of information faster and easier than before.

The Internet may be regarded as an electronic library. It includes a great deal of up-to-date information on food related topics such as recent food laws, health and safety information, recipes and consumer issues.

Home shopping for food can now be done on the Internet. A customer can look through a store's lists of goods and place an order. The shopping will be delivered at a convenient time to both supermarket and customer.

Electronic Point of Sale (EPOS)

This is the system used at every checkout in supermarkets. Every product has a barcode that is unique to that product. When scanned at the checkout, the barcode identifies the product, the price and itemizes the till receipt. All this information is transmitted to the computers in the File Maintenance Depot (FMD) that records the daily sales of all products. This allows the supermarket to manage their stock. The computers in the FMD update stock levels overnight. They transmit the stock information to the distribution depots, which can then re-order stock and deliver it to the store as and when it is needed.

The EPOS system can ask questions of the checkout operative. For example, if there is a barcode scanning error, the computer asks if it is correct. EPOS also allows customer numbers to be checked daily, and the length of the customer queue can be reported. Information on the average spend per customer and the average basket size is all stored in the computers.

Modelling bacterial growth

A computer software programme called Food MicroModel has been designed by the food industry. This programme models bacterial growth in food products, and it can predict the ways in which food spoilage bacteria will grow under certain conditions. It is possible to model the changes that could occur within the product and provide a prediction of what could happen if there was a delay in the distribution and delivery of the item.

▪ Things to do ▪

1. Using a computer, draw up a specification for a chicken dish that would be suitable for a meals-on-wheels service.
2. Using a nutritional analysis software programme, work out the nutritional value of your dish per portion.

The use of ICT in the production of Flavour Fresh Salads

Aims

- To understand the use of computers in the management of quality control.

Flavour Fresh Salads Ltd is one of England's largest tomato growing companies. The company distributes high quality tomatoes to the country's leading retail outlets. In the height of the season they grow, grade, pack and distribute approximately 86 tons of tomatoes every week.

Computers are an essential part of the firm's production process. They are used in a wide variety of ways, from the development of the product specification through to the distribution of the tomatoes to retail outlets.

Using the Internet and E-mail

The Quality Control Manager accesses current information about food law using the Internet. The manager uses the DEFRA (Department for Environment, Food and Rural Affairs) website (www.maff.gov.uk). DEFRA is a government department that provides information about foods and the pesticides used in the food industry. This information is essential to the Quality Control Manager who must check that the tomato plants are being given the correct type and amount of pesticides.

The company has also found that E-mail is an effective communication system. Different departments within the company communicate with each other using internal E-mail and this enables quick decision-making, for example, if a problem arises with the distribution system or a meeting needs to be arranged with several managers.

Growing the tomatoes

There is also a very sophisticated computer system in the office of the greenhouse manager. This computer controls:

- the temperature of the greenhouses
- the different kinds of feed
- the atmosphere
- humidity
- the flow of water to the plants.

If a problem arises the computer identifies the source of the problem and alerts the manager so that the necessary action can be taken.

Grading the tomatoes

The grading and quality of the tomatoes is also computer controlled. Once the product specification has been agreed by the company and the retail buyer, the computer system on the automatic tomato grading machine is programmed to meet the specification. It checks each tomato according to the following criteria:

- weight
- size
- shape
- colour
- density.

The tomatoes arrive in the warehouse from the greenhouses and are put onto the tomato-grading machine. The tomatoes fall on to a moving grading belt. This has a series of holes that are the correct diameter for the specific variety of tomatoes and according to the required specification.

As the tomatoes pass along the conveyor belt a weight sensor weighs them and each batch of tomatoes has ten photographs taken to record the colour, shape, size and density. This whole process is computer controlled. The tomatoes are then packed according to the specifications.

Using EDI

Orders come into Flavour Fresh via an EDI system. Information and adjustments to orders can then be dealt with immediately.

A computer controls the warehouse temperature, and temperature probes are used to check the lorries before they deliver the tomatoes.

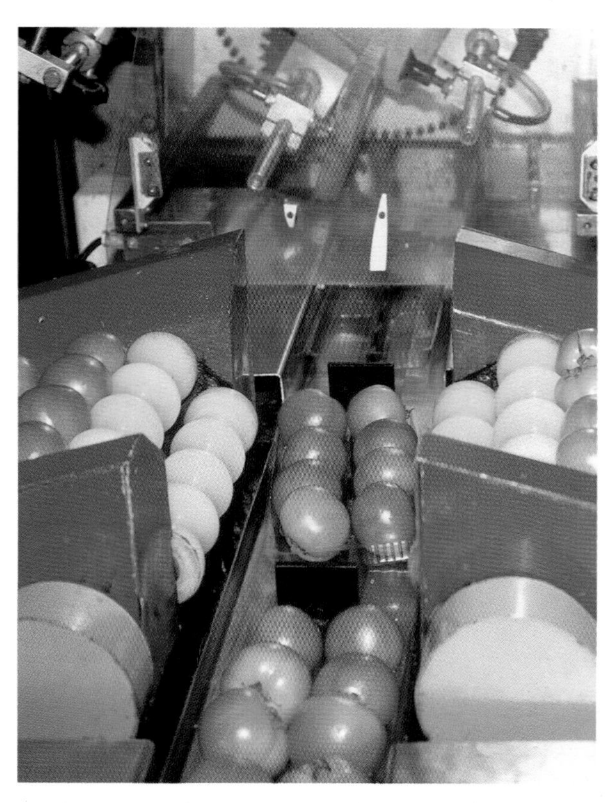

The automatic grading machine

Things to do

You are going to simulate a production or assembly line!

1. Select a team of operatives from your class to work on an assembly line.
2. As a team, decide on a food product which can be made in bulk, within the constraints of your food technology room.
3. Identify each process the food product has to undergo and where the critical control points are.
4. Plan the layout of the production or assembly line and include quality checkpoints.

   Use a computer to help you do this.
5. Identify the key workers on the production or assembly line.
6. You will need to appoint a production line manager and someone to be in charge of:
   - the equipment needed
   - ordering the ingredients
   - quality control
   - **critical control points**
   - preparation of raw ingredients
   - assembly of ingredients
   - the cooking or chilling process
   - the final product.
7. The manager must ensure each member of the team knows his or her role in the production of your product.
8. Use the production line to produce a batch of the product.
9. Time each stage of the operation.
10. Time the whole process.
11. Evaluate your work.
    - Was the quality control and critical control points carried out efficiently?
    - Were there any problems in your production line? How were they solved?
    - Was the final product of good quality?
12. Using a spreadsheet, cost your final product. This cost is to include labour costs.

    Decide on an hourly rate for each member of your team.

The use of CAD in batch and volume production

Aims

- To understand the use of computer aided design (CAD) in batch and volume production.

■ Things to do ■

1. Collect samples of different types of paperboard food packaging.
2. Analyze the packaging to see how it was made. Choose one product and draw the net for the packaging using a CAD programme.
3. Describe the purpose of each element of the packaging for your chosen product.

   Explain why you think the packaging material is suitable for the product.

Computer aided design is used in the food industry for designing and making packaging, 2D and 3D **modelling** of the product and its packaging, and for the management of design data generally. The use of CAD enables different colours and images to be tried out easily on screen to find the most appropriate design.

2D modelling

2D modelling can be used in industry and at school for designing nets for food packaging. The net is a 2D shape which, when cut out, can be folded into 3D packaging. Once a design is finalized, the information can be transmitted from the computer to a card-cutting machine. If you have access to a plotter-cutter you could use it to cut out card to the shape of the net for the package you have designed.

In industry a net profile is multiplied many times and the computer is able to plan the nets in such a way that they maximize the use of the paperboard as efficiently as possible. This ensures that there is very little waste. Packaging net design has to be very precise to ensure that the packaging can be folded up correctly. After they have been cut out, the nets are separated from the paperboard sheet and then assembled. All the artwork and labelling requirements (designed using a CAD package) will have been included on the paperboard prior to the manufacturing of the packages.

3D 'virtual products'

Computer software is now available to create 3D virtual food products on screen. The products can be viewed from all angles. This helps the product development team visualize and manipulate the product to see how it will look when finished. DATA in conjunction with the All Saints Trust have produced a CD-ROM virtual reality tour of a pie manufacturing plant called 'Pie in the Sky'. This allows the user to explore all areas of the food plant and access specific pieces of equipment to see how they work.

In industry, 3D modelling can save the time, materials and money needed to make prototype products for batch and volume production.

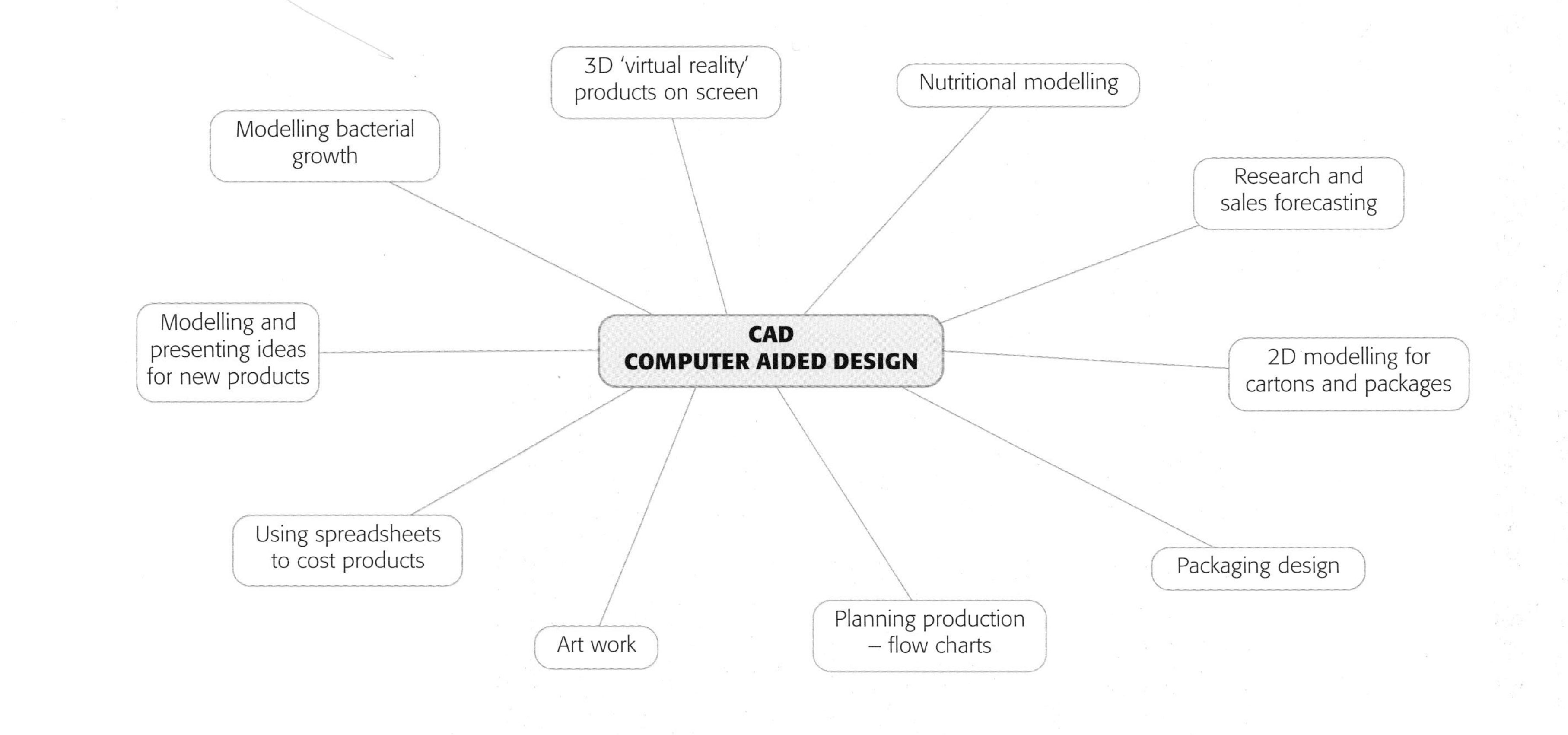
CAD
COMPUTER AIDED DESIGN
Modelling bacterial growth
3D 'virtual reality' products on screen
Nutritional modelling
Research and sales forecasting
2D modelling for cartons and packages
Packaging design
Planning production – flow charts
Art work
Using spreadsheets to cost products
Modelling and presenting ideas for new products

CAM in batch and volume production

Aims

- To understand the use of CAM in batch and volume production.

Computer Aided Manufacture (CAM)

CAM is the use of computers by manufacturers to help them monitor and control the automatic production of food products. The computers aid the production of food, based on set specifications and **tolerances**. This enables manufacturers to pinpoint faults and, when necessary, to adapt the process to achieve quality products. Computers may be used at some or all of the stages of food production.

Electronic sensors are used to monitor changes in the food and this information is fed back to the computer. An example of using CAM in food production is cake-making (see Case Study 4 on page 72).

Sensors are used to test for things like:

- weight changes in the product
- temperature changes in mixers, ovens, cooling ovens or freezing units
- changes in colour
- tolerance levels for weight and dimensions
- moisture content of products
- the humidity of cooling ovens.

CAM equipment can be very sophisticated and efficient. It can speed up manufacturing processes, but it is also extremely expensive. It can run continuously 24 hours a day, seven days a week and will stop only if there is a major fault in the system.

Designers of CAM systems often work with food manufacturers to produce computer programmes that will meet their specific needs. The computer programmer enters data specific to the individual processes involved and the manufacturing operations can be carried out via computer links. All the movements and processing of raw materials, semi-finished and finished products can be planned, designed, executed, inspected and monitored using CAD and CAM systems.

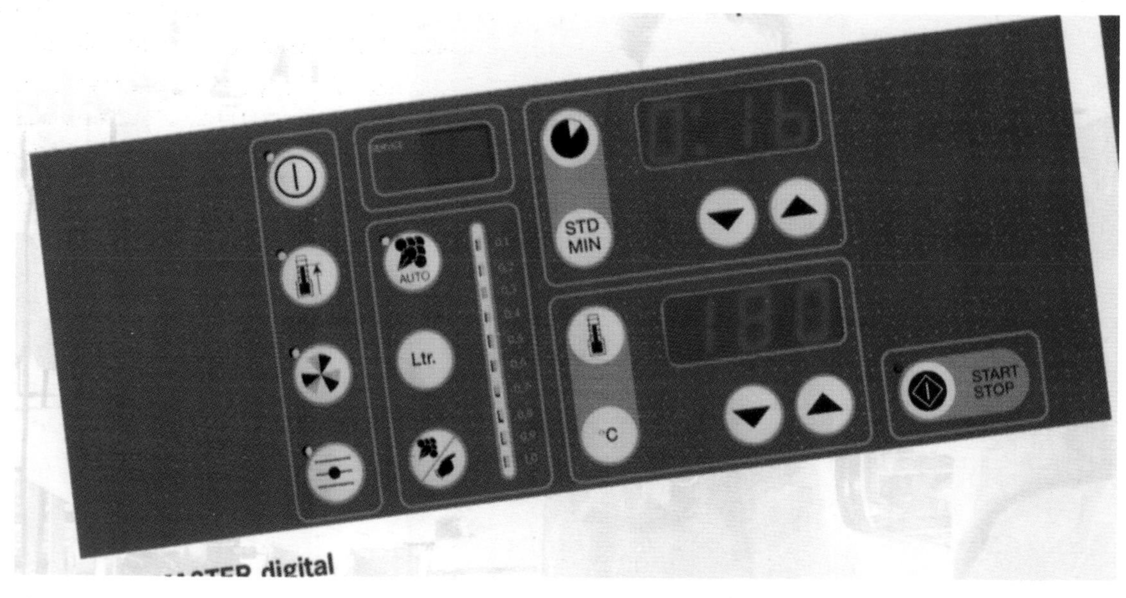

The computer control panel of an oven. Sensors regulate the temperature and humidity of each oven shelf

Computer numerical control (CNC)

Computer numerical control (**CNC**) literally means the control of machines using numbers or digital information. The machines are used for fast, accurate and repeatable production processes. CAM systems often use CNC machines to carry out tasks in the production process. CAD software can be used to drive CNC machines, such as card cutters for producing packaging.

The benefits of CNC machines are:

- products are made accurately and quickly
- they provide increased flexibility as they can be used in batch and mass production systems
- they can be used for continuous operations or in conditions that are hazardous to human operators
- they are economical to operate but at a high set up cost.

Automatic production

Many processes that are controlled by computer are automatic. For example, in bread production, temperature control is very important throughout the process. If ingredients deviate from the specified temperature, heat sensors will inform the computer system of the problem. The system will then adjust the temperature automatically and there is no need for human intervention.

Robotics

A robot is a piece of equipment that is computer driven and mimics the skills of human beings. Robots are CNC machines. They are used for 'pick and place' operations and are designed to perform specific functions such as gripping small, hot, fragile or soft components. They are used in the food industry for packing biscuits into trays, and for placing and stacking full boxes of food products.

However, as was seen in Case Study 4, some tasks are not suitable for automatic computer-controlled equipment and have to be done by hand, for example, placing cherries on top of Bakewell Tarts.

Computer Integrated Manufacturing systems (CIM)

When all stages in a food production process are integrated and controlled by computer systems this is known as CIM. The computers are linked together in a network and control both the machinery and the flow of information during the manufacturing process. The mass production of products such as bread, cereals and snack foods use CIM systems (see Case Study 5 on page 74).

CIM systems are essential in mass production because they enable manufacturers to produce a high volume of products quickly. Manufacturers also know that the system is highly accurate for repeated production processes and will therefore produce a consistent product.

Things to do

1. Using the information gathered when you simulated a production line (see activity on page 81), explain which aspects of your process could be computer controlled.
2. Produce a table listing the advantages and disadvantages of CAM systems in food manufacture.
3. A medium-sized bakery decides to introduce a CIM system for the mass production of bread. In a small group, discuss the impact that this decision might have on the bakery's workforce.

Practice examination questions

1 What is batch production? Give two examples of food products made by this process.

2 Computer Integrated Manufacture (CIM) is used when making bread.

a Describe three processes in CIM when making bread.

b Describe two quality controls used in bread production.

c Why is a feedback system important in control systems?

3 a What is meant by HACCP?

b Explain the importance of HACCP procedures in food manufacturing.

c Explain why yogurt and cheese samples are sent to the microbial laboratory every day.

4 Explain the importance of electronic links, such as E-mail and the Internet to a food manufacturer.

5 a Explain the meaning of:

i **Quality Assurance**

ii Quality Control.

b Describe and explain four quality control checks to ensure that Cherry Bakewell Tarts are the same shape, size, weight and colour.

6 Flow charts are important because they can clearly identify critical control points (CCP).

a List six CCPs in the production of cheese.

b For each CCP, describe one way in which the hazard can be monitored, controlled or prevented.

7 a Explain the difference between a low-risk area and a high-risk area.

b Explain why food handlers in the low-risk area must be separated from the high-risk area.

8 Beefburgers appeal to both adults and children and provide protein and energy.

They may be eaten as a snack or as part of a main meal. Two specification points for the beefburgers are:

- well shaped
- quick to cook.

a Give three more specification points that would be included in the final specification for these beefburgers.

b Name three ingredients that may be used to make beefburgers, and state their function. Explain why the ingredients you have chosen are suitable for this product.

c Modify a recipe for a beefburger, by adding two new ingredients for flavour and texture, so that it is suitable for summer barbecues. Explain your choice of ingredients.

Section D:
Design and market influence

The effect of technology on society and individuals

Aims

- To understand how technology affects society and our everyday lives.
- To recognize that new technologies have advantages and disadvantages.

Values

Cheap food has recently become a controversial issue because of BSE and the foot-and-mouth crisis in 2001. Public concern means that the food industry has to ask itself difficult questions about the relationship between the cost of food and its safety and quality.

Discuss the impact of BSE and foot-and-mouth disease on the food industry. What are the key issues? What impact do food scares have on people's buying and eating habits?

Technology shapes and influences our everyday lives more than ever before. From the moment we wake to the moment we turn out the light to sleep, technology is involved in many of the things we do.

Developments in technology

Developments in technology have contributed to labour, time and energy saving equipment in industry and the home. As consumers, we are now able to freeze and re-heat foods in a matter of minutes using the microwave, or programme a bread maker to assemble, cook and produce fresh bread without any human input. The food industry has become highly technical, relying heavily on **CAD/CAM, CIM** and **CNC** equipment. These systems and equipment enable faster, more flexible and cost-effective manufacturing. Other developments within the food industry include new:

- preservation methods
- packaging methods
- **primary** and **secondary processing** techniques
- distribution and storage.

Developments in technology have also led to increased product reliability and the implementation of better safety standards. Improved technology systems used in the manufacturing process have led to products being more consistent in terms of their quality and **sensory characteristics**. The safety standards now implemented in food manufacturing are thorough and reliable and this has been assisted by the implementation of **HACCP** (see pages 54-5). This system was introduced in 1990 and it has been one of the main contributors of increasing food safety and product reliability.

New technology has also been employed to help the food industry to produce cheap food.

New technology has also enabled the consumer to have a wider and more varied choice of products. This is mainly due to:

- increased opportunities for food import due to better transport, storage and packaging
- the development of modern food materials and processes
- the use of biotechnology.

The development of modern food materials and processes

Synthetic flavours

These are copies of natural flavours, but they are easy to create and cheaper than using natural flavours. Synthetic flavours are used in many products such as yoghurts, almond essence, low fat products, soups and sauces. Synthetic flavour is sometimes added to enhance the attractiveness of some foods that are lacking in natural flavours. The main disadvantage of using synthetic flavour is that the food may no longer be considered natural. Consumers can see when synthetic flavours have been used by reading the label. They are identified by E numbers (see page 16). The Flavourings in Food Regulations 1992 lists specified flavours that are permitted only in limited amounts. This regulation also gives guidelines on how the synthetic flavour should be labelled.

The permitted use of artificial chemical **additives** and their use in food manufacturing have increased the attractiveness, **shelf life**, quality and acceptability of a range of products. On the other hand, the additive E102 (tartazine) found in soft drinks has been linked to hyperactivity in young children.

Modified starch

Starch usually requires a hot liquid before it will create a gel (see page 42). Modified starch (starch treated with acid or alkali) has been developed chemically so that it will form a gel with cold water or milk. A modified starch is therefore beneficial in the manufacture of instant desserts, mousses, toppings, sauces, soups and gravies.

Antioxidants

Food manufacturers now add antioxidants to some food products to prolong their shelf life. Antioxidants prevent fruit and vegetables from turning brown. They also inhibit the oxidation of fats, which can make fatty foods like oily fish turn rancid. Some antioxidants (vitamins C and E) are naturally occurring in some foods and may be added to others (for example, adding lemon juice to bananas to prevent them turning brown). Sulphur dioxide is a chemical antioxidant. It is often added to dried apricots.

Values

Some people say that the benefits of using permitted additives outweigh the disadvantages to the few people who have been badly affected by additives.

Read the booklet on food additives produced by MAFF and carry out your own research using the library and the Internet. What is being done to ensure the safety of chemical additives? What are your views on the use of food additives?

Biotechnology

Biotechnology itself is not new. It has been used throughout history to make useful food products. For example, bread is produced using yeasts. Yeast is a living organism that interacts with flour, water, sugar and heat to make bread rise. This is a biological process (see page 42). Cheese making is another example. The reaction of rennet with milk to produce curds and whey (see page 68) is also a biological process, employing the activities of an **enzyme**. Other examples of biotechnology in food manufacture include the production of yoghurt, salami, vinegar and pickles.

Biotechnology also involves the breeding of plants and animals to improve desirable characteristics. These days this can also involve genetic modification (GM). The genes contained in every cell of every living thing control the characteristics of that organism. Genetic modification is the altering of genes to produce new characteristics.

GM yeasts and rennet

One example of genetic modification has been carried out on yeasts. These have been genetically modified so that they can be used in the processing of a variety of foods. The genetic code of enzyme chymosin (found in rennet) has been identified and altered. This genetically modified enzyme is now suitable for use in vegetarian food, but it works in the same way as the enzyme that comes from animals.

The benefits of GM are:

- it can make food crops resistant to pests and diseases
- it can control weeds during crop production
- it can increase the quantity (yield) and quality of food produced
- it can improve the nutritional value of foods.

GM can be used to enhance the protein content of crops. Fruits and vegetables can be modified to contain increased levels of vitamins and minerals. Wheat can be modified to be gluten free, and maize and soya beans can be modified to alter their **saturated** fat content.

The genetic modification of major crops is already taking place in the UK and around the world, for example:

- insect and disease-resistant apples are being developed
- GM melons and tomatoes ripen more slowly and therefore have a longer shelf life
- GM potatoes are also disease and insect resistant, as well as having a higher starch content
- rice has been genetically modified to have a higher **iron** and vitamin A content. This rice was developed to help reduce vitamin A deficiency among people in India.

GM may also be used to alter the genetic make up of animals. The aim for the food industry would be to develop animals that would produce, for example, higher yields of milk or better quality meat. Cloning (the process of producing a genetically identical offspring from the cell of a parent animal) may be developed to produce many animals with exactly the same desirable characteristics. Cloned animals may be used to develop new medicines for humans.

Values

Genetic modification has caused great concern. It raises both ethical and safety issues. For example:

- Do people have the right to interfere with nature in this way?
- Are GM foods safe to eat?
- Should all GM foods be labelled and do consumers have the right to be told that the food they buy has been genetically modified?
- What impact will GM foods have on developing countries?

In a group, discuss your views on these matters. Carry out some research on the Internet or in the library. What are the arguments for and against GM food?

Technological processes

Myco-protein

The production of myco-protein is an excellent example of how new technology has brought new food products to the market. Myco-protein is more commonly known as Quorn. It is a good source of protein, low in fat and **cholesterol**, and high in **non-starch polysaccharides (NSP)**. Quorn was first commercially produced in the 1980s and it can now be bought in many forms: chilled and frozen, chunks, mince, fillets and sausages. The biological technology used to produce Quorn works on the same principles used when making beer or in the production of yoghurt. This process of fermentation requires correct environmental conditions, so the temperature and pH value is closely monitored.

Food products made from Quorn

CAD/CAM (see pages 78-85)

Computer systems are widely used to produce large quantities of food products safely. Computer systems can also make the food business more effective and efficient. The use of CAD/CAM technology therefore benefits both the food industry and the food consumer.

CAD/CAM make the food business more effective and efficient because:

- CAD systems are used to produce packaging that is both appealing and informative.
- CAD and other computer software may be used to make business activities like market research, marketing, purchasing and distribution more effective and efficient. This can make the business more profitable, help to reduce costs, as well as helping manufacturers give customers what they need and want.
- CAM systems help production match consumer demand. Production lines can adapt to increases or decreases in demand. This improves efficiency and reduces waste.
- CAM systems help to ensure the consistent quality demanded by customers.
- Increased efficiency and waste reduction mean that food may be produced more cheaply. These cost savings can be passed on to customers.

CAD/CAM help make food safer because:

- CAD and CAM systems can help to detect faults and hazards in food production (for example, foreign objects in food, dangerous increases in temperature, rapid bacterial growth rates).
- CAM systems help manufacturers follow the food regulations, so that they achieve higher standards of food safety.
- Information on packaging allows consumers to make an informed choice when they buy food products.

Values

Are there any disadvantages to the use of CAD/CAM systems in the production of food?

- Is cheap food always a good thing?
- What effects has computer technology had on the work force in the industry?
- Does the use of computer technology always benefit the consumer?
- Do CAD/CAM systems have an environmental impact?

■ Things to do ■

1 Make a list of all the technological pieces of equipment in your food technology room. Choose four and list the advantages and disadvantages of each one.

2 Create a table to summarize the advantages and disadvantages of new technology in the manufacture of food products.

3 Visit your school canteen and observe two pieces of large-scale technological equipment being used. Explain how they work and describe the ways in which they make the production of school lunches cheaper and more efficient.

4 Collect four labels from food products and identify the additives used. Use the booklets about food additives produced by the Food Standards Agency (www.foodstandards.gov.uk) to help you.

5 a Define the term genetic modification.

b Outline the ethical issues that are associated with GM foods.

c Hold a classroom debate on the issue of genetic modification.

Moral issues

Aims

- To recognize that moral, cultural and environmental issues are an important part of designing and making food products.

When designing and making food products, food technologists must consider moral, cultural and environmental issues, as well as the needs of the **target market group**. They have a responsibility to consider the impact that their products will have on society and on individuals. Consumers are increasingly concerned with a number of issues that can influence the types of food produced and the way they are made. These issues include:

- factory farming
- GM food development
- sustainable technology
- conservation of resources
- cultural concerns.

Moral issues are important in the designing and making process because some of the issues can affect health, safety and general well being. In addition, media coverage has raised public awareness of food-related issues. This means that food manufacturers must consider these issues if they are to meet consumer needs successfully. Some current moral issues affecting food production are:

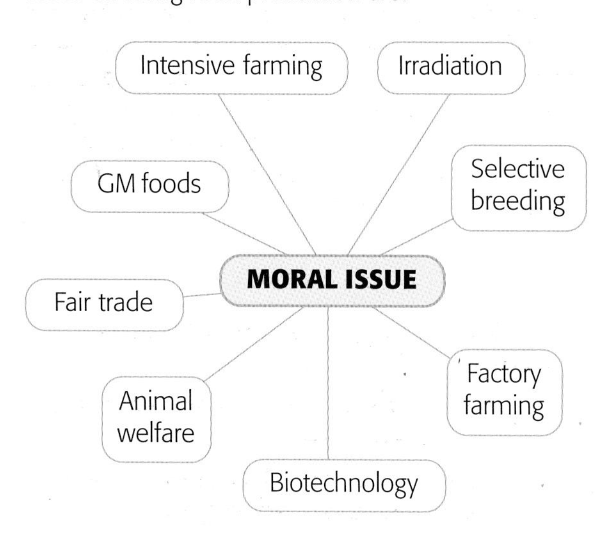

Selective breeding

Selective breeding produces faster growing chickens, hens that lay more eggs and cows that produce more milk. The effects of this type of breeding on animals raise moral issues. Here are two examples of the effects of selective breeding:

- The broiler chicken reared for meat and not eggs reaches its slaughter weight in 42 days. This puts an excessive strain on its heart and lungs and its overweight body can result in lameness.
- Egg-laying hens have been selectively bred to produce 300 eggs a year and this puts a huge strain on the hen's calcium reserves. This can actually cause brittle bones in the egg-laying chicken.

Values

Do you think it is right that animals should be affected in this way in order that more food can be produced more quickly?

Factory farming

There are several organizations that have been established who are against factory farmed animals; Compassion in World Farming, Advocates for Animals and Friends of the Earth. The conditions in which factory farmed animals are kept are distressing and alarming to some people. Conditions are often cramped with poor ventilation, limited lighting and no room for the animal to exercise or move freely. Factory farming can also cause problems with disease and the spread of infection because lots of animals are kept crowded together.

Fair trade

Much of the food we buy is produced in developing countries. Workers in some of these countries are often very poor and do not receive their fair share of the huge profits being made by large multinational companies. The Fair Trade foundation was established to help developing world producers of products such as tea, coffee, cocoa, bananas and honey. The foundation tries to ensure that profits made from selling these products are divided more fairly between the producers and the companies that retail the products.

Conditions of factory farmed animals are often distressing

The foundation has its own display label, which is only awarded to third world companies that give their producers a fair deal. By purchasing Fair Trade products you will be contributing to improved living, health and financial conditions in developing countries.

The management of GM food development

The development of GM foods was examined on pages 88-91. GM foods raise several moral issues:

- Are GM foods safe to eat? There are strict controls on the production of GM foods (see the Food Standards Agency website). However, some people say that we don't know enough about genetic modification, and we do not know the long-term effects of eating GM foods.
- Should all GM products be labelled to show that the food contains genetically modified ingredients? What rights should consumers have in this respect?
- How will producing GM foods affect the environment? Some people say that modified genes could 'escape' and transfer across species which would have unknown results. However, there are regulations to control the production of GM crops and trials are being carried out in the UK and around the world to find out what the risks (if any) actually are.

It is clear that GM foods have many potential benefits for the food industry and for consumers. However, many people are very concerned about possible dangers. We do not yet know if GM foods are a good thing. Scientists are continuing with research and entering in to the debate with governments, the food industry and consumer groups.

■ Things to do ■

1 Working in a group, choose one of the moral issues outlined above.

a Summarize the arguments for and against the issue you have chosen.

b Set up a debate with half the group for the issue and the other half against it.

Remember that it is important to listen to each side of the discussion before you decide how to vote. Try to be objective.

Environmental issues

Aims

- To recognize that environmental issues are an important part of designing and making food products.

Concern about the protection of the environment has become a major issue for many people. Consumers and pressure groups are now demanding products and packaging that do not damage the environment. Manufacturers are responding with improved processing techniques, more environmentally friendly packaging and a more sustainable food supply. Some manufacturers now make environmental protection and sustainability a priority. There are two aspects to the environmental issue.

Sustainability

During the last century humans have used new and increasingly powerful technology to exploit the Earth's resources. As a result, supplies of natural resources like oil, coal, minerals and fresh water are likely to run out in the future unless action is taken now.

The population of the world is increasing rapidly. Feeding such a large population is becoming a major issue because the amount of land suitable for agriculture is decreasing. Many people in the world are starving, while others overeat and throw away large amounts of food. Sustainable food production will be a real challenge for the future.

In order to support sustainability, food manufacturers need to find ways of:

- using more energy-efficient processes and reducing the consumption of resources like water
- using sustainable resources, for example, those that can be replaced through recycling (paper, glass and some metals), or by using renewable resources like softwoods from managed forests for paper and card
- reducing waste and using the by-products of food production, like whey, for other purposes
- using processing techniques and preservation methods to avoid waste, prolong shelf life and preserve food supplies.

Pollution

The second major environmental concern is pollution. The manufacture of food products can cause a great deal of pollution. For example:

- Some food processing methods can cause air pollution, water pollution and effluent.
- The manufacture of packaging for food can cause damage to the environment.
- A large proportion of household rubbish consists of food packaging.

Food manufacturers are taking pollution issues very seriously and taking action to reduce the environmental impact of their activities.

Packaging

Food packaging affects the environment in two ways:

- using resources like minerals, oil and wood to produce the packaging
- creating pollution as a result of packaging disposal.

The food industry is addressing the problems caused by packaging by recycling, redesigning and reducing the amount of packaging used.

Recycling.

Packaging made from glass, metal and paper can all be recycled. Some plastics may also be recycled. However, it is difficult to recycle packaging made from mixed materials (for example, packaging consisting of layers of metal foil, plastic and card) because it is difficult to separate out the different layers. Packaging designers therefore need to consider using materials that can be easily recycled. They also need to use materials that have already been recycled, like recycled paper. However, it is up to consumers, not manufacturers, to make sure that packaging is actually recycled and not just thrown away.

Glass

Glass is an excellent packaging material in this respect. Recycling glass uses less energy than producing new glass. It can also be recycled over and over, which means that it need have very little impact on the environment once it has been made.

Metal foils and cans

Recycling aluminium and tin cans can greatly reduce pollution in our environment. Both can be recycled indefinitely and can be reformed into food containers. There are well-developed systems for the recycling of these products, but collection and sorting is labour intensive.

Paper and card

Paper and card is widely used to package goods and it can actually be recycled five times before the paper fibres weaken. The conservation of paper would therefore greatly reduce the impact of food manufacture on the environment. Waste management systems designed specifically for the collection and recycling of paper is common these days. The only real disadvantage of paper recycling is that recycled paper is often of a lower standard than virgin paper.

Plastics

Making new plastic uses oil and gas reserves and can result in air pollution. Recycling plastic can greatly reduce these problems. Specialist waste management systems are in operation to recycle the seven different types of plastic used for packaging. The waste generated during the manufacture of plastic packaging (for example, trimmings from plastic tray production) can also be reprocessed.

Reducing the amount of packaging used

Reducing the weight and wall thickness of packaging can use less material. For example, plastic bottles are now a third lighter than they used to be and the yoghurt pot is now half its original weight.

Designing new types of product and packaging

Designers are developing efficiently shaped packaging and refillable packaging. Manufacturers can produce larger unit sizes that reduce the amount of packaging per production run of a product. Some products are being produced in a more concentrated form so that they last longer.

Educating the consumer

Manufacturers can encourage consumers to buy food products in reusable packaging. They can also support recycling and promote this to customers through labelling and advertising.

Food manufacture

Food manufacturers can also help to protect the environment by redesigning their production processes.

Reusing by-products

By selling on the by-products that result from producing a food product waste can be drastically reduced. For example, cheese manufacturers sell on whey to baby food companies to be used in dried milk. Cream and butter are also produced from whey. ~~Damaged bread from Warburtons is sold on to pig farmers for feed.~~

Improving efficiency

Manufacturers can help to protect the environment by using computerized control systems for:

- weighing operations
- recipe control
- controlling the adding and mixing of ingredients
- temperature control in preserving and processing.

Accurate measuring and controlling processes like these can help to reduce waste and energy costs. Automating labour intensive processes using CIM, robots and so on can reduce labour costs, reduce human error and speed up the processing time.

The future

Protecting the environment should be seen as a partnership between the consumer, designer and the manufacturer. It is important to examine the environmental impact of every stage of the food production process, from farming practices in raw material production to packaging the final product. Food product designers need consider all aspects of the process when designing a new product in order to identify opportunities for reducing environmental impact.

Recycling glass, paper and tins

■ Things to do ■

1. Your challenge is to identify ways in which the Food Technology department could recycle the waste and packaging created through practical work. You will need to identify the different types of waste produced and the packaging used. How can it be collected and stored safely in the food room? To widen awareness of your work, prepare and perform an assembly about your project. You could also write an article for the local paper.
2. Research the processes for recycling glass and metals. Use the Internet or library to help you. Produce a **flow chart** showing the life of a glass bottle or tin can, from the time it is first used, through the recycling process, to its return to the food manufacture for reuse as packaging.
3. Contact a local food manufacturer and ask them how they reduce and manage the waste they produce. What other actions do they take to protect the environment?

Cultural issues

Aims

- To recognize that cultural issues are an important part of designing and making food products.

People today have many opportunities to experiment with and try new foods. Food programmes on the television, holidays abroad and our multi-cultural society all influence the food we eat. As our food knowledge and tastes have become more multi-cultural, so to have the range of products produced by the manufacturers. The wide range of foods from different cultures and to suit different tastes can be seen in the fresh and raw ingredient section as well as in the ready meal section of the supermarket. Examples range from herbs, pastes, marinades and chutneys to sushi, Halal and Kosher meat. Food has never been so interesting.

Religious beliefs

Some cultures and religions have specific food requirements. Some foods are not permitted because they are considered 'unclean' or 'sacred'. Some groups also require food to be prepared in a certain way, in accordance with guidelines set out by their religious beliefs and traditions. Food manufacturers must take these requirements into account.

The Jewish faith

Judaism is a long established religion and one that follows strict food rules in terms of preparation and consumption. Food that is consumed within this culture must be Kosher. This means that it is ritually acceptable, and also means that it follows the rules in the Torah (the Jewish Holy Book). Jewish food law forbids the eating of certain foods and classes foods into two types: dairy and meat. They must be kept totally separate in preparation, cooking and consumption. The following foods can be eaten as they are Kosher:

- Mammals that chew the cud and have spilt hooves (sheep and cows). + lamb)
- Birds that are domesticated (chicken, ducks, geese and turkeys).
- Fish that have scales and fins.

However, the following are not Kosher and are therefore considered unfit to eat:

- Mammals which do not have split hooves or chew the cud (pig and rabbit). + camel + horse
- Wild birds and birds of prey.
- Shellfish and eggs from non Kosher birds.

Some Jewish food products

Gefillte fish in a savoury sauce is a traditional dish of Jewish origin, usually eaten as an evening meal on the Sabbath (which is a Friday).

Red peppers stuffed with minced beef is an ideal main course product that could be served with salad or potato chips.

Fruit tree is a sweet product that is very suitable to be eaten at the festival of Rosh Hashanah.

Manufacturers have responded by producing special kosher ranges of foods which meet Jewish requirements and which are certified by Rabbis. There are now many catering companies that have been established just to provide Kosher foods for Jewish celebrations.

The Hindu faith

Hindus are mainly vegetarian and they do not eat beef, as the cow is considered a sacred animal. Milk and milk products are eaten, but strict Hindus do not eat meat, fish or eggs. They do not drink alcohol. Hindus are generally very traditional in the preparation and cooking methods used.

The Muslim faith

Muslim food law is very strict, eating pork and shellfish is totally forbidden. Muslims consume a lot of lamb. However, a special ritual known as Halal must be used to prepare all meat. Regular fasting is required, particularly during the month of Ramadan. Muslims are not allowed to drink alcohol. Traditional meals are often hot and spicy.

Some Muslim food products

Spicy lamb curry served with rice and onions.

Spinach and chana dhal. This makes a good vegetarian accompaniment to almost any main meal.

Sheekh kebabs. These minced lamb kebabs are delicious, served in pitta bread or a salad.

The picture below shows a Halal shop where Halal products may be purchased.

A Halal shop

Food from other countries and regions

Consumers are increasingly cooking, buying and eating food from many different countries. Indian, Chinese, Italian and American food is widely available in supermarkets and restaurants. Food from Japan (sushi), Thailand (green chicken curry, lemon grass and fish sauce) and Mexico (enchiladas and refried beans) is fashionable and commonly found in high street retailers. Chefs are now producing 'fusion' foods that combine ingredients and methods taken from several different countries. In fact, Indian food is now so popular that chicken tikka masala has replaced fish and chips as the UK's favourite food.

Vegetarians

There are three types of vegetarians:

1. Lacto-vegetarians. They will eat milk and cheese, but not meat, poultry, fish or eggs.
2. Ovo-lacto-vegetarians. They will consume milk, cheese and eggs, but not meat, poultry or fish.
3. Vegans. They will only eat plants and will not consume any food that is of animal origin.

When designing food products for vegetarians, it is important to remember that not eating animal products may lead to a diet deficient in certain **nutrients**. The nutrients in which vegetarians are likely to be deficient are iron and vitamin B12. Alternative sources of iron are pulses, green vegetables and cereals. Alternative sources of vitamin B12 include **fortified** breakfast cereals and yeast extract.

A vegan diet means that no protein is consumed by eating meat, fish, milk, cheese or eggs. The vegan can find alternative protein from Quorn, textured vegetable protein, soya, cereals and pulses.

The cultural influence on food design and manufacture

There are many different cultural influences on food design and manufacture. In addition to those described here, our culture now includes, for example, many single person households, people who choose to eat only organically grown food or have a low fat diet. There are many other cultural influences that arise from lifestyle choice, religious beliefs and regional traditions.

Each of these influences can represent a potential market for the food manufacturer. It is vital that food designers understand the different cultural requirements of their target market group. Research is important when designing new food products, particularly when designing products for those whose faith includes strict food laws. Clear labelling is also important in a multi-cultural society.

■ Things to do ■

1. A culture can be any group of people who share the same ideas, beliefs and traditions. Brainstorm as many different cultures as you can think of. Choose one and create a mood board that reflects and captures the spirit of that culture. Display your mood boards in your food technology room.
2. Research Halal and Kosher foods. Describe the rituals associated with these terms.
3. Design a new ready meal for young single people. What are the key lifestyle factors that you will need to consider, for example, gender, income, skills, leisure activities?
4. Carry out a survey at your local supermarket. Using the following list of cultures, list all the products that you may purchase for each of them. Which do you think is the most fashionable at the moment? (For example, Indian, Chinese, Italian, Thai, Mexican, Japanese, American.)

Product analysis

Aims

- To understand why product analysis is an important part of product development.
- To understand how to analyze a product.

What is product analysis?

Food technologists analyze food products in order to understand them and to give them ideas for new products. Product analysis involves several activities:

- **disassembly** – taking a product apart, reading the labels, tasting it and evaluating attributes like the way it is made, its ingredients and specification;
- research – finding out how a product is made and finding out what consumers think of it;
- evaluation – assessing things like product quality, environmental impact, moral and cultural attributes.

Product analysis is about examining food products closely, asking questions, testing products to find the answers to those questions and evaluating the results.

Who analyses food products?

Food designers carry out product analysis. A designer creating a new product will want to analyze similar products made by other companies. By doing this the designer will be able to improve on what is already available and design new features for the product to make it different from the competition.

Product analysis is also important for trading standards officers, students, and consumers. Trading standards officers analyze products to check quality, manufacturers' claims and to ensure products meet legal health and safety requirements. Students can use product analysis to help them learn about food products. Consumers carry out simple product analysis every time they visit a supermarket. They will consider some or all of the following criteria:

- What does the product look like?
- What is the product designed to do?
- Who is the product designed for?
- Is it safe for that consumer to eat?
- Does it match the consumer's own moral/cultural values?
- Is the product value for money?

Why is product analysis important?

Product analysis is important because:

- it helps students understand how food products are produced;
- it helps with the design of new products and can help to design efficient production processes;
- it helps manufacturers produce products that will sell successfully;
- it helps ensure that products are of good quality and are safe to eat;
- it helps consumers select the product that is right for them.

What is a quality food product?

Many different factors make up the quality of a product. When thinking about quality you are asking yourself 'How does this product perform against my chosen criteria?' You are asking questions like:

- Does it taste, look and smell as it should and does it taste, look and smell good?
- Is the product fresh?
- Does it use ingredients that are of a good quality?
- Is the product good value for money?
- Does the packaging keep the food fresh, does it promote the product effectively and can it be recycled?

If the answer to these questions (and many more) is 'Yes' then you have a quality food product.

Product quality can also be a matter of opinion. For example, one consumer's view of a quality product many not be the same as another consumer's view on the matter. This is why consumer research is an important part of product analysis.

Product analysis criteria

The following list gives a range of criteria that may be used when assessing a food product. Remember that you may have to tailor your criteria and the questions you ask to the particular product you are analyzing.

- *Product description* – what is it?
- *Target market group* – who has the product been designed for? What are their characteristics? How has the product been promoted to this market?
- *Function* – What has the product been designed to do?
- *Ingredients* – What is the product made of? What is the function of each ingredient?
- *Product data* – Weight, size, volume, nutritional profile, construction and so on.
- *Production methods* – What processes have been used in the production? Why have they been used?
- *Packaging* – How has the product been packaged? What is the purpose of the packaging?
- *Safety issues* – Ingredients, packaging, shelf life and storage.
- *Texture* – What does the product feel like, in the mouth and on the fingers?
- *Flavour/Aroma* – What does the product taste/smell like?
- *Appearance* – What does the product look like?
- *Freshness* – How fresh is the product? Does it look and smell fresh?
- *Value for money* – Will the target market group think the product is worth the price? How does the price compare with similar products?
- *User perceptions* – How do consumers assess the product quality?
- *Moral values* – Does the product contain ingredients that are GM or irradiated? Does the product have a Fair Trade label? If not, why not?
- *Environmental issues* – Is the packaging recyclable? What environmental information/advice does the manufacturer give to the consumer?
- *Cultural issues* – Is the product designed to reflect the food of a particular country or region?

Differences between quality of design and quality of manufacture

When assessing the quality of design you are considering things like:

- How well it meets the needs of the target market group – including value for money, shelf life and safety.
- How well the finished product matches the original design specification.
- The choice and proportions of the ingredients.
- Whether it does what the manufacturer claims it will do.
- The design of the packaging – does it protect the product? Does it promote the product effectively?
- The moral, environmental and cultural aspects of the product.

When assessing the quality of manufacture you are considering things like:

- A product's appearance, taste, smell, sound and texture.
- Is the quality consistent?
- Does the product meet legal requirements for safety?
- The quality of packaging construction.

■ Things to do ■

1. Choose another example of a one-off product, a batch product and a product produced in volume and analyze them using the criteria that have been identified.
2. Explain why it is important to analyze and evaluate products.
3. Research the different types of pastry that could be suitable for a meat and potato pie. Discuss the suitability of each one.
4. Set up a taste panel to test three types of bread – 1) from a small local bakery, 2) bread produced using **batch production** methods and 3) bread produced in high volume (for example, Hovis). Analyze the three breads using the criteria used in this section.
5. Explain why the consumer should ensure a lasagne is thoroughly heated through.
6. Brainstorm ten other products that could be produced using volume production techniques.

Planning and processing 1

Aims

- To understand the importance of planning in the manufacturing process.
- To understand the difference between quality of design and quality of manufacture.

Planning for production in industry is essential to ensure that the products produced are safe, of a consistently high quality and that they are cost effective. Planning for efficiency when manufacturing in quantity means that the process involves:

- as few steps as possible,
- is automated where possible,
- is as fast as possible.

Planning involves setting out a sequence of the activities involved in the production process. A process or system can be broken down into three main stages:

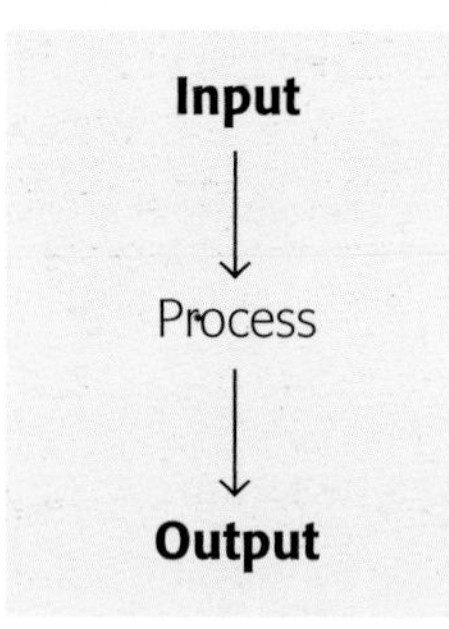

These three parts make up a system. The input section of the system includes:

- raw ingredients,
- workers,
- the machinery.

The process part of the system includes:

- assembling,
- mixing,
- processing,
- cooking,
- cooling,
- packaging.

The output part of the system includes:

- the finished product,
- storage before transportation to retail outlets.

Read Case Study 2 Singleton's Dairy again (pages 68-9). Their system for producing cheese can be show as a diagram or flow chart:

Input	Raw milk, **bacterial culture**, vegetarian rennet, machinery and workers.
Process	**Pasteurization** ↓ Culture added ↓ Rennet added ↓ Separation of curds and whey ↓ Whey drained off and curd cut into chips ↓ Chips put into moulds and pressed ↓ Pressed cheese taken out of moulds and wrapped in cheese cloth ↓ Cheese waxed and vacuum packed
Output	Finished cheese stored ↓ Cheese dispatched to retailers

This diagram is a simple description of the system. If you read the case study you will see that the cheese-making process is more complicated than this. Making cheese also involves things like temperature control, time control, hygiene control and control of the quantity of ingredients and the activity of the **bacteria**. When planning a system, the food technologist must make sure that it includes these controls.

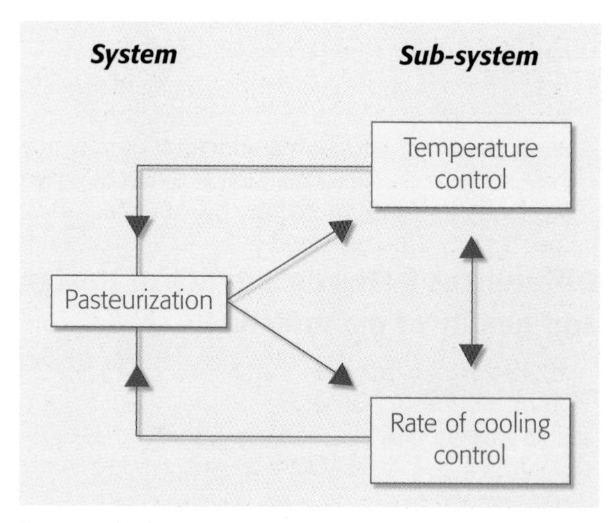

System and sub-system

Control and feedback

Singleton's Dairy knows that the process of pasteurization (stage 1 in the system diagram above) requires that the milk is first heated to 71.7°C and then rapidly cooled to 10°C. The system therefore needs to include a process that monitors and controls the heating and cooling of the milk. This is known as a sub-system. The sub-system ensures the milk is heated to the correct temperature, and will feed back information on the temperature of the milk and the speed of the rapid cooling process. Manufacturers often use computers for sub-systems that monitor, control and **feedback** information (see CAM on pages 78-9).

Critical Control Points (CCPs)

Controlling the temperature of pasteurization is important because at 71.7°C harmful bacteria are destroyed. Bacteria in milk are a hazard (a danger to the consumer). It is therefore vital for health and safety reasons that the temperature is controlled at this point in the cheese-making system. When designing a system the food technologist will identify these **critical control points** and ensure there is a sub-system in place to eliminate, reduce or monitor a hazard. The case studies on pages 66-7 include other examples of critical control points. For example, in the production of yoghurt, the wall dividing the **low-risk area** from the **high-risk area** represents a critical control point.

What is quality control?

In addition to avoiding health and safety hazards, the food technologist must control the quality of the product (see page 50 for a definition of a quality food product). **Quality control** is the system employed by the manufacturer to ensure that the quality of the product is maintained throughout the production process. It involves a series of checks, to ensure that at each stage the product is reaching the required standard. The final product is then finally checked against the original criteria set out in the specification.

Many checks are carried out throughout the production process by specialist machinery and by the production worker. Some of these checks include:

- Raw material checks – manufacturers often buy their raw ingredients from a supplier who will have produced them according to the manufacturer's specification. They will need to be checked prior to entering the manufacturing area.
- Weight checks – many food production systems require careful checks on the weight of ingredients, the weight of the product at various stages of production and the weight of the final product. Computer-controlled scales usually measure weight electronically. These scales are extremely accurate and help achieve a consistent result.
- Temperature checks – controlling temperature is vital in many food production systems. Manufacturers will control the temperature of raw material and finished product storage. Cooking temperatures are monitored and controlled in computer-controlled oven tunnels (see page 84). The core temperature of food products is tested with a temperature probe.
- Time checks – these also a very important part of a production system. Production runs happen to strict schedules and deadlines.
- Metal detection – this is used to check if any metal fragments large or small have fallen into a product. Metal in food products may mean that there is actually a problem with one of the machines.
- Microbiological testing – this can be undertaken at the manufacturing plant, but, more often than not, sample products are sent to independent microbiological testing laboratories. Results are then documented and copies sent back to the manufacturer.
- Other checks – in addition to these checks, manufacturers may use sensors that can check a product's humidity, moisture content, size, shape and consistency of colour.

Although computers carry out many quality control checks these days, there is still a place for human quality control. Production workers often undertake visual checks like grading and sorting as these checks often cannot be carried out as successfully by computers.

Checking the final product

In addition to the checks carried out before and during production, the finished product is also checked. Sensory testing of sample products is carried out to ensure that the products being produced are reaching the required criteria on the specification. If there is a problem the information will be fed back throughout the production system and the source of the problem identified. Products that do not meet the required standard are rejected. This is wasteful so it is important to:

- carry out quality checks at critical control points during the production process;
- ensure problems are identified and remedied quickly.

Quality assurance

Food manufacturers are keen to give consumers an assurance that their products are of a high quality. Quality control systems enable them to do this.

Things to do

1 Name and explain the three main stages of a system.

2 Using a case study other than Singleton's Dairy, produce a flow chart that summarizes the production system for the product described.

3 a Explain what a critical control point is.

b Identify a critical control point in your flow chart and describe how the hazard is eliminated, reduced or monitored.

4 Explain the difference between quality assurance and quality control. Discuss the importance of each in the manufacturing process.

Planning and processing 2

Aims

- To understand how to simplify the production of a product

After identifying the input, process and output, the manufacturers add in all the necessary checks. The example here is an industrial production plan for chicken tikka.

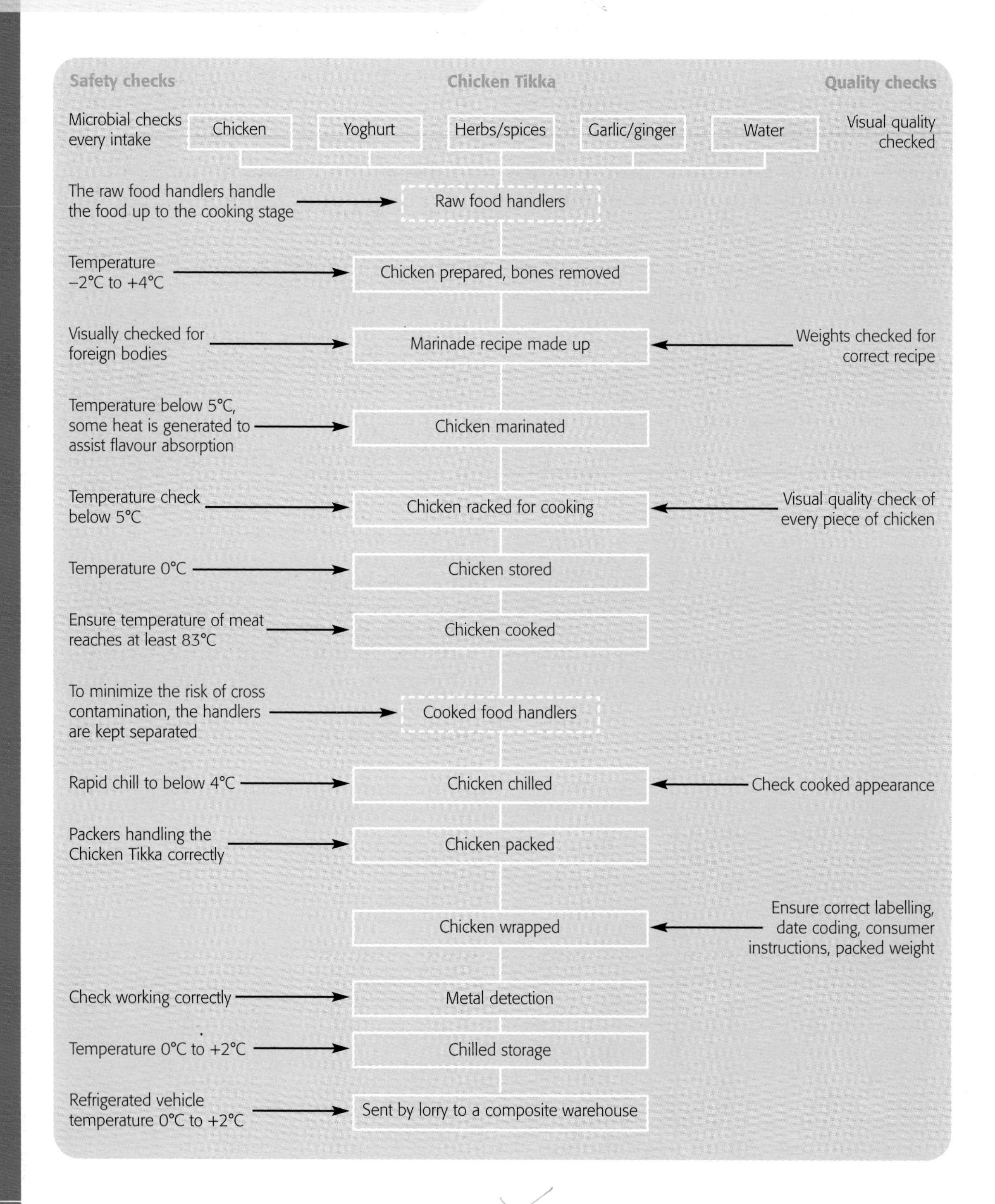

Raw ingredients

500g raw chicken; 1 large tub of greek yoghurt; 2 cloves of garlic; 25g of fresh ginger; 1 tsp of chilli powder; 2 heaped tbls of chicken tikka paste.

Safety	Method	Quality
Check all equipment required is in good working order.	Organize ingredients, equipment. Wash hands and wear protective clothing. Pre-heat oven to gas mark 6 (180°C).	Ensure ingredients are from reliable source and within the correct date. Visual check.
To remove any contamination. Use hot, soapy water to wash in, avoiding cross contamination.	Cut and trim chicken. Put waste in the bin. Wash board and knife.	Cut chicken into similar sizes to allow for even cooking. Remove any sinus/bones. Put rubbish in the bin.
	Assemble marinade – mixing remaining ingredients. Waste control.	Mix thoroughly - even distribution of additional components. Ensure all waste is in bin.
Cover with foil and place on the bottom shelf of the fridge.	Place prepared chicken in marinade. Cover and place in the fridge for 20 minutes.	Spread out in the dish to allow for even cooking.
Utilize protective equipment when checking hot foods.	Place marinated chicken into a deep baking dish, cover with foil and bake for 35–40 mins. Removing foil after 20 mins and stir.	Use temp. probe to check chicken (high-risk food) over 65°C.
Refrigerate after $1\frac{1}{2}$ hours if not consumed.	Allow chicken to cool slightly, before garnishing and serving.	Arrange garnish attractively

This second production plan has been simplified and shows how the same product might be made in a domestic kitchen. Notice there are still safety and quality checks to follow.

▪ Things to do ▪

Design a savory product that conforms to dietary goals and complete a production plane for your idea. Identify the input, process and output. Draw a production plan and label it clearly.

Practice examination questions

1 Discuss how technology used in the food manufacturing business affects the choice, cost and variety of foods available.

2 Explain how CAD/CAM can be used to produce food products in quantity and cheaply.

3 Explain how the consumer can take responsibility for the environment within their own home in the following areas:
   a purchasing of goods
   b packaging
   c waste control.

4 Factory farming and GM are causing concern with the population in general.
   Explain the reason for this.

5 Name two advantages of GM and two disadvantages.

6 Explain Fair Trading and why it could be viewed as a moral concern.

7 Discuss how food manufacturers have met the dietary needs of our multi-cultured society.

8 Formulate a criteria that could be used to analyze and evaluate a range of products.

9 Discuss why planning is crucial in the manufacturing environment.

10 List five checks that can take place during the manufacture of a product and explain the reason for each.

11 Discuss why production planning in industry requires more detail than a domestic production plan.

Full-course coursework

What to expect

- You can develop a project idea based on a topic set by your teacher, select from a list of set coursework tasks or develop your own project idea.
- You will be expected to produce a food product and a 15–20 page A3 design folder.
- You should spend up to 40 hours on your own project. Check with your teacher to see how many lessons you will have over how many weeks. Knowing how much time is available will help you plan and organize your project successfully.

How will it be assessed?

- The coursework project accounts for 60 per cent of the marks for the full-course.
- Your project is assessed using the designing and making criteria shown in the table opposite, *Full-course assessment criteria*.

Designing and manufacturing

During your course, you will be asked to analyze commercial products to see how they are designed and manufactured. Analyzing products will help you understand issues related to user needs and moral, cultural and environmental issues. Product analysis is therefore a very useful activity because it can develop your understanding of the design and manufacture of high quality products.

When you undertake coursework, the designing process will help you develop:

- skills of problem solving, including moral, cultural and environmental issues.
- communication techniques using a variety of media, including the use of ICT.

When you undertake coursework, the making process will help you:

- explore and practice a variety of manufacturing techniques.
- be imaginative and experimental when combining materials.
- use CAD/CAM where appropriate and available.
- demonstrate your understanding of industrial practices.

Using the coursework section

The following full-course section will take you through the assessment criteria, describing how to achieve the best marks. You should, therefore, refer to this section of the book as and when you need to.

	Assessment criteria	Marks
1	Identify needs and use of information sources to develop detailed specifications	9
2	Develop ideas from the specification	27
3	Use written communication and graphical techniques	9
4	Produce and use a detailed working schedule	9
5	Select and use tools, equipment and processes to make a product	39
6	Devise and apply tests to check the quality of the product	9
	Total marks	102

Full-course assessment criteria

Coursework project design folder

Your design folder should be concise and only include information that is really relevant to your project. This means that you will need to be very selective about what to include so that you can target the available marks. Your folder should consist of approximately 15–20 A3 pages and should include a contents page and page numbers to help in its organization. The table below gives a suggested guideline for the page breakdown. However, your folder contents may vary slightly from this because of the type of project you may have chosen.

Contents	No of Pages
Front cover	Extra page
Contents page	Extra page
Identifying needs and use of information sources to develop detailed specifications	4–5
Develop ideas from the specification	6–7
Use written communications and graphical techniques	Throughout
Produce and use a detailed working schedule	1–2
Select and use tools, equipment and processes to make a product	3–4
Devise and apply tests to check the quality of the product	1–2
Total number of pages	15–20

Coursework project folder contents

1 Identifying needs and use of information sources to develop detailed specifications

This section describes how you will produce a detailed brief based on the needs of the target market group. It describes how you will select and use information from a wide range of sources and helps you to produce a design specification for your product.

Identifying needs

At the start of your project you will have to try and identify a realistic need or problem that:

- interests you
- you can find enough information about
- enables you to demonstrate your knowledge and understanding about food technology.

Your need or problem may be based on a topic set by your teacher, be selected from a list of set coursework tasks or be your own idea.

- Whatever starting point you use, the need or problem that you identify must enable you to develop and manufacture a food product.
- The key to identifying a realistic need is to explore user needs – not any old users, however, but those in a target market group. In other words, you will not be designing for yourself, but to meet the needs of other people. It is said that a new product is only successful if the target users actually need it, want it and will repeatedly buy it.

Even if you are given an outline project brief by your teacher or if you choose a set task, you will still have to find out about user needs – partly because it is a requirement of the assessment criteria, but also because design work is easier when you do not have to make all of the decisions yourself!

It is important to discuss your project idea with your teacher to make sure it will cover all the assessment criteria. This will give you the opportunity to gain the most marks.

Designing for people

Although new products are developed for all sorts of different reasons, it must be remembered that all products are designed for people. This means taking into account the needs and values of potential users of your product – finding out about the kind of food they already eat and their likes and dislikes. As a designer, you must therefore be very clear about who you are designing for – your target market group.

Working in teams

Finding out about consumer needs and values are ongoing activities for most food technologists. Many technologists work in teams, which use a mixture of market research, analysis of information and discussion to identify opportunities for developing new food products. A design brief can then be produced.

Working as a team is a good way to explore the food needs of people in different situations. For example, your team could spend ten minutes brainstorming:

- the kind of target market group you could design for – are they vegetarians, sports enthusiasts, young children or busy students?
- the kind of food products they like to eat.

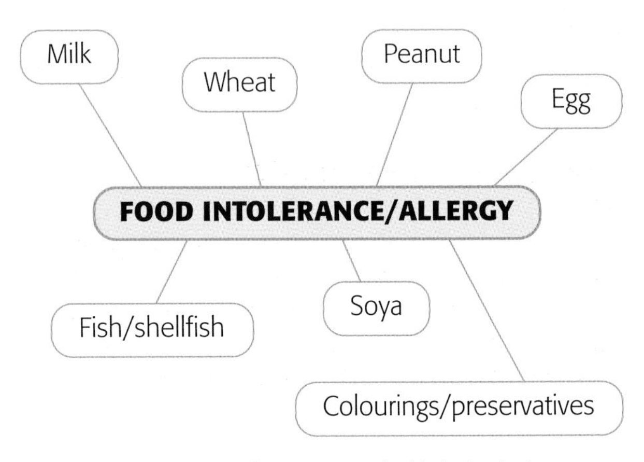

This student produced a brainstorm to highlight foods that cause allergies in some people

■ Things to do ■

Making decisions at the start of a project is always very difficult. Working in a team is an ideal way to thrash out ideas. It can provide just the support you need to get started. You could try:

- brainstorming user and market needs.
- identifying where to find information.
- gathering information and reporting back to the team.
- bouncing ideas off other people.

Asking questions

Whatever starting point you use for your project, you will need to ask questions about the need for the food product you intend to design and make. For example:

- What are the needs of users of the product? For example, their age range, food needs, leisure activities and lifestyle.
- How would the food needs of target market group's change in winter or summer? What if the users were very old or very young?
- What kind of food product would satisfy the needs of these users? What level of nutrition should the product provide?
- What kind of similar food products are there already on the market? How much do they cost?
- In what situation will the product be eaten? For example, is it a family dish, something to eat at picnics or for school dinners?
- What are the latest trends in eating? For example, is pasta still popular or are organic foods gaining ground?

Developing a design brief

Asking questions about your product idea and potential users in your target market group should help you to write a design brief. This will not only focus your mind on what you are going to design and make, but should help you to plan your research. Your design brief needs to be simple and concise and should explain:

- what needs to be designed (a new kind of dessert? A main course rice dish?)
- who it is for (vegans or vegetarians?)
- any special user requirements (nutritional, cultural, religious or economic?)
- the benefits the product could bring the users (easy to eat on the move? Easy to prepare?)

Your design brief is very important because it will help you pinpoint the information you need to collect in order to design and develop your product idea. Other useful ideas include:

- underlining the key words in your design brief.
- making a list of the questions you could ask about the key words.
- using these questions to help you plan your research.

■ Things to do ■

You might be given a context in which to design and manufacture a product. For example: 'A food manufacturer has approached you to design and make a new low fat food product. Their market research has shown that young people are more interested in eating healthy-option foods.'

As a team, discuss how you would approach this project. What information would you need to find out about:

- the target market group?
- existing low fat foods?
- the new product?

To be successful you will need to justify the needs of a target market group and produce a detailed brief. *(3 marks)*

Gathering information

You will need to gather relevant information from a wide range of appropriate sources, if you want to gain maximum marks. The key to success is to be very selective in what you research and to only use information that can really help you make decisions about what you are going to design and make. Remember you only have 15–20 pages for your coursework folder, so do not pad out your work with interesting but irrelevant facts! If you have a lot of information, summarize it using diagrams and charts.

Your design brief should help you plan your research, which may include the following sources of information:

- market research – a shop survey of similar existing food products
- a consumer survey – a questionnaire to find out the needs of your target market group
- product analysis – to find out about similar existing food products
- a visit to a manufacturer – possibly using the Internet, videos or a CD ROM
- a product test report – such as *Which* magazine or from the Good Housekeeping Institute
- a database or CD ROM – to find out about nutritional information
- leaflets from supermarkets and information from textbooks.

You do not have to use all these information sources, but do try to use those that are most helpful. Three different sources should provide you with enough information to enable you to write a design specification.

Remember you only have 40 hours for your project, which may limit some kinds of research you can do. It is not always possible, for example, to write off for information to companies and get a useful response back in time. It is often more effective to find out information from published material, such as leaflets and books, through videos or the Internet. Market research and product analysis are also very successful techniques for targeting the information you need to find out.

Market research

Gathering information from consumers is called market research. It is used to identify the buying behaviour, taste and lifestyle of potential customers. For example, a survey can establish the brands of products different age groups buy regularly, the types of foods they like to eat and the amount of money they are willing to spend. New products can then be developed to match customers' needs.

Using product analysis

Many food technologists use product analysis to develop specifications for new products. You can compare similar products already on the market, analyze labels and packaging and use sensory analysis to find out:

- about ingredients, processes and nutritional information
- how and why the product appeals to the target market group
- the price range that customers will pay.

Use the information you find out from product analysis to develop specifications for products. This can be very helpful when developing a specification for your own food product.

To be successful you will need to select and use information from a wide range of appropriate sources. *(3 marks)*

Producing a specification

You should analyze your research information and select what is useful. Be very selective – remember you have around 4–5 A3 pages for the whole of this section. Once you have analyzed your research information, you will have a clearer idea about the food product you want to design and make. You are now ready to write a design specification, which should give details of the product's form, function and budgetary constraints. In other words, your food specification should describe:

- the product type and its purpose
- the requirements of the target market group
- nutritional information
- the type of ingredients to be used
- the portion size
- the price range of the product
- the scale of the production
- safety factors, such as the expected shelf life of the product
- environmental issues.

Your design specification should give you a clear structure to work to and will guide your thinking about the food product you are developing. It should have enough detail to enable you to generate a range of ideas, but leave some room for creative thinking.

You should refer to your specification criteria when evaluating your initial design ideas. Your specification will gradually change during your product development, until you reach your final design specification. Do not delete your initial specification, since the examiner will want to see how your design thinking has developed.

Specification

My food product must:

- be a nutritious, filling, savoury product that could be served in the school canteen.
- appeal to vegetarians and meat eaters.
- include fibre and protein and be a good source of vitamins.
- use fresh, tasty and colourful ingredients, with a variety of textures.
- provide enough kj/kcal per portion for a growing teenager.
- cost between 70-90p per portion.
- be suitable for small batch production.
- suitable for freezing with a shelf life of three months.
- use a heat resistant food container that can be recycled.

Your initial specification could look something like this

■ Things to do ■

'Super Stores' have asked you to develop a new potato product to be sold from the chill counter. The target market group is mothers of young children.

- Develop a design specification for this product.
- Develop a specification for a similar product that appeals to teenagers.

Specifications in industry

Manufacturers of commercial food products often develop specifications from existing products. Standard specifications are often based on the following criteria:

- raw material (ingredients and standard components)
- recipe (for example, for 20 000gm)
- methods of manufacture
- manufacturing process flow diagram
- HACCP (critical control points)
- microbial analysis (to detect the presence of bacteria)
- packaging information
- shelf life (use-by date)
- product finished weight or volume
- sensory specification (for example, 'crunchy texture')
- instruction for use.

To be successful you will need to produce a specification that describes form, function, user requirements and budgetary constraints. *(3 marks)*

2 Develop ideas from the specification

This section describes how you will present a range of realistic and imaginative ideas. You will then develop, model and test your design ideas to produce a realistic design proposal. You will also review your ideas as they develop against the specification.

Generating ideas

Generating a range of realistic and imaginative ideas is worth up to twelve marks, so it is really something that you can get your teeth into! You should spend time developing and evaluating your ideas. This will give you the opportunity to display your creativity and design abilities.

Realistic ideas are ones that can be designed and made in the time available to you. You only have 40 hours for the whole project, which means that you will need to be very focused on what you have to do. Look for suitable dishes or recipes that you can develop to meet the requirements of your specification. You could use:

- research information about user and market requirements. For example, which ingredients or types of meals are popular?
- information about existing products. Can you design something new or original?
- recipe books, magazines and menu planning software to inspire ideas.

Produce alternative ideas

You need to present at least three alternative ideas, so choose products that use different materials, processes and working techniques. Your ideas should be realistic and workable, but also challenging. Be imaginative, do not just settle for dishes you have cooked before, but choose dishes that demand a high level of practical skill.

Experiment and choose dishes that will test and stretch your practical abilities. For example, if you were designing a sweet food product suitable for young children, it would be:

- unwise to develop a vanilla all-in-one sponge, a chocolate all-in-one sponge and a lemon all-in-one sponge. This product range would not stretch your design and practical abilities.
- better to develop a range of items, such as a pastry fruit slice, an all-in-one cake and a swiss roll (whisked sponge). This would give you the opportunity to develop a full range of skills.

Things to do

Try basing your ideas around a theme, inspired by cultural, social or environmental issues, such as:

- festivals
- disco food
- 'going green'
- finger foods
- 'snack attack'
- five-a-day.

Presenting your ideas

Clearly present your ideas using simple labeled diagrams or pictures of the food product. You should explain why and how each of your ideas meets the requirements of the target market group, so you are able to judge its market potential. This can be done by evaluating each of your initial food product ideas against your specification criteria. You could compile your results in a table, such as the one below. You can then produce a summary of your evaluation to explain which of your ideas best meets the specification criteria and why.

Specification criteria	Idea 1	Idea 2	Idea 3
Nutritious, filling, savoury product	√	√	√
Suit vegetarians and meat eaters	√	X	√
Include fibre, protein and vitamins	X	√	√
Tasty, colourful and textured	√	√	√
KJ/kcal per portion for growing teenager	X	√	X
70–90p per portion	√	√	X
Suitable for small batch production	√	√	√
Freezable with three month shelf life	√	√	X
Recyclable heat- resistant container	√	√	√

Evaluating food product ideas

To be successful you will need to present a range of realistic and imaginative design ideas.*(12 marks)*

Developing and modelling ideas

Having evaluated your outline ideas, you now need to develop and model them further. This activity is worth up to twelve marks, so do not forget to check how much time is available to you.

You can model your ideas by trialling the production of each dish. Your trial production should include details of:

- ingredients and quantities
- tools and equipment
- the method of making, with timings
- HACCP
- quality checks.

Remember to make a note of any problems that occur when you model your product ideas. If you have the opportunity to take photographs of your product modelling, this will not only provide evidence of your work in your folder, but will give you a reference point for further development.

Testing ideas against the specification

Modelling your product ideas will enable you to test them against your specification criteria. You can then decide which is the best one to take forward as you final design proposal.

You will need to devise a means of testing your food products against the specification criteria. This may involve the use of comparative tests, setting up a tasting panel or using sensory analysis tests. Comparative testing is useful for comparing the difference in taste between food products. It can involve paired or triangle tests – comparing two or three products.

Using sensory analysis

Sensory analysis involves the testing and evaluation of food against sensory characteristics (organoleptic qualities). Sensory analysis makes use of sensory descriptors, such as appearance, aroma, texture and taste. Tasting food is essential when you are designing food products for other people – or when you are cooking for yourself.

You should taste and test all your food product ideas against your specification criteria. For example, if you are designing a savoury product for the school canteen, use the words from your specification, such as nutritious, filling, fresh, tasty and colourful. Star profiles are very useful for recording the results of tasting.

Setting up a tasting panel

Setting up a tasting panel is a good way of finding out the views of users in your target market group. This may involve asking people into school or organizing a tasting elsewhere. Check with your teacher on how you could organize this.

In order to achieve a fair tasting, you need to first plan and set up your tasting tests, using sensory analysis. Give people equal food samples at the same temperature. Ask them to record their views using star diagrams, hedonic ratings or tasting charts.

Make sure that you write the results of your sensory testing. Are your products the same as or better than products already on the market? How well do they meet the specification criteria? What are the views of your target market group?

Modifying your product idea

Once you have evaluated your food product ideas, you will know which is (are) the most successful. You are now at the stage when modifications may be necessary so they fit the specification better. Could you combine the best aspects of each idea to produce a best solution? Modifications to your product ideas may involve:

- reducing the cost of ingredients to make the price more attractive to your users.
- making the product more nutritious or healthy, for example, reducing the fat, salt or sugar content, or increasing the NSP.
- changing the ingredients to improve the flavour, texture, aroma or appearance.
- increasing or decreasing the portion size.
- altering the preparation of ingredients or the shape or decoration of the product.

The final design proposal

Testing your design ideas should provide you with enough information to develop your final design proposal. You may need to:

- combine the best aspects of each idea to produce the best solution.
- modify your ideas and repeat the trialling and testing processes. This will enable you to test the feasibility of your modifications.

You may need to modify your design specification to match the requirements of your final design proposal. For example, you may have specified that your product should be of a size 'to fit in a sandwich lunch box'. If your product shape is not the right size, you may have to amend the specification criteria.

You should record the results of all your trialling, tasting and testing. Your final design proposal should clearly meet all your specification criteria. Remember to give reasons why this is the best product design.

To be successful you will need to develop, model and test design ideas to produce a realistic design proposal. *(12 marks)*

Review your ideas

It is very important to evaluate your ideas at all stages of your product development. The examiner will hope to see your evaluative comments throughout your design work, as this forms the basis of developing a successful design proposal.

Your evaluations should be objective. Being objective means basing your evaluation on actual results, rather than being biased towards your own opinions or feelings. For example, if you tested your product ideas and you preferred the one with the mushrooms, but the users in your target market group preferred ham, you have to follow the preference of the users. They are the ones who may buy the product! Your evaluative comments should therefore come from a number of different sources, such as your peers, the target market group or 'experts' (like your teacher!).

Things to do

Describe the methods you would use to objectively evaluate your food product ideas.

To be successful you will need to review ideas as they develop against the specification. *(3 marks)*

3 Using written communication and graphical techniques

In this section, marks will be awarded for clear written communication, using specialist vocabulary. You will use graphical techniques and other media with skill and accuracy. You will also use a range of appropriate ICT techniques.

Written communication

The marks for written communication can be picked up throughout your design folder. You should aim to use specialist and technical language related to food technology in all the writing that you do. Your use of specialist language must be accurate and your writing clearly presented with information set out in a logical way.

For example, one student used the following language to describe a biological aspect of her work:

Before the biscuit dough is mixed, the starch and protein molecules in the flour are separated. During mixing, the protein molecules unfold and link around the starch molecules and the protein strands form a matrix or network. The linked protein molecules are elastic and allow the dough to stretch.

What you write reflects your knowledge and understanding about food technology. High quality writing should form the basis of your design folder. For example, your design brief, specification and the evaluation of your ideas will be written. When you annotate your design ideas, report on product testing or produce a working schedule, you will have the opportunity to demonstrate your understanding of specialist technical terms and identify specific material and manufacturing processes.

Your folder work can be either hand or computer generated. You will be given credit for high quality work whichever way you produce it – either by hand or by using computer software.

To be successful you will need to clearly communicate information in a logical and well-organized manner, using appropriate specialist vocabulary. *(3 marks)*

Other media

Good quality communication skills are essential if you are to demonstrate your product ideas, knowledge and understanding to others, including the examiner. There are many different ways of communicating ideas, other than simply writing. For example, you could use any of the techniques and media listed below.

- Graphical techniques, for example, bar charts, pie charts or star profiles.
- Brainstorms, for example, in the form of a spider diagram.
- Tables, for example, nutritional analysis tables, costings, tables showing HACCP and quality control points.
- Flow diagrams, for example, to show manufacturing processes and the order of assembly.
- Photographs, using either film or digital methods.
- Cut and paste from magazines, for example, for developing design ideas of packaging ideas.
- Sketching by hand, for example, for products, packaging or labeling.

To be successful you will need to use graphical techniques, photographs, cut-outs, models and mock-ups appropriately with a high degree of skill and accuracy. *(3 marks)*

Information and communications technology (ICT)

You may have the opportunity to use ICT to enhance your food technology work. You should provide evidence of your use of ICT in your coursework folder, although you will not lose marks if you produce work by hand. The use of ICT can help you collect, compile and analyze information and record your findings. It can also help make your design folder look smart and professional.

Word processing

Word processing software is very useful because it enables you to undertake a variety of activities. It produces well presented, easy to read work. You can write text, design questionnaires, edit, change and save your work. Hand written work can be just as effective if written clearly in black ink.

Other types of software can be used to help with the presentation of your work. For example:

- desktop publishing is useful for designing page layouts and for combining text and images. Work can be stored, cut, pasted and saved.
- clip art can sometimes be used to add graphics to image boards to show your food product ideas.
- flowcharts can be produced using a word processing program using the 'drawing' tools.

Spreadsheets

Spreadsheets are very useful programs. They can help you:

- calculate and display nutritional information about products.
- undertake product costing.
- calculate the scaling up or down of recipes.
- display the results of questionnaires using charts.
- display the sensory characteristics of food products on a star diagram.

Databases

Many databases are available on CD ROM, including recipe databases and nutritional databases for recipe adaptation and modification.

Digital cameras

These are ideal for recording practical work in progress, as well as your finished product. Images can be stored in your computer program and incorporated into your work as and when you need.

▪ Things to do ▪

Investigate the use of computer software in your school. Experiment with different types of programs to find the most useful. Try to incorporate ICT in your coursework.

Using ICT

Look out for the opportunities to use ICT in any of the following activities.

Research

- Use a database or CD ROM to search for nutritional information.
- Use the Internet to find up-to-date information about nutrition and health, food guidelines and legislation, food materials, existing products, market trends and lifestyles.
- Use survey software or a DTP package to generate questionnaires and results.
- Use a spreadsheet to analyze research information. This makes it easy to produce charts, diagrams or graphs to present the results of research.

Presenting ideas and planning manufacture

Use a digital camera or scanned images to produce sources for ideas.

- Use specialist software for nutritional analysis.
- Use a CAD package to produce images of food, to produce templates for cutting or for packaging designs. Logos and images can be scanned into the computer and modified.
- Use food-modelling software to produce 'virtual' 3D products.
- Use a spreadsheet to cost a product, calculate production in quantity, to analyze the results of comparative tests, tasting tests or sensory analysis.
- Use HACCP software simulation to plan risk assessment.
- Use computer-generated flowcharts to plan manufacture.

Product manufacture

- Use CAM to make food of repeatable quality, such as using a bread maker for identical loaves.
- Use a digital camera to record the sequence of making and testing your project.

Presenting your work

You must present your work to the best of your ability. Take time to plan the layout of each page, since you only have 20 pages in all to present your work.

- Check the accuracy of tables and charts and make sure they are clearly labeled, so the examiner understands your intentions.
- Sketches or diagrams of food products or packaging should include measurements if they are relevant to the product.
- Make sure that you take time to set up photographs, so your food product is shown to its best advantage.
- Check that photographs are in focus.
- Digital images should be printed on high quality paper.

To be successful you will need to use a range of appropriate ICT techniques skillfully. *(3 marks)*

4 Produce and use a detailed working schedule

This section describes how to produce a systems diagram, explaining the inputs, processes, outputs and feedback, showing where performance checks are made. It helps you produce a working schedule for your product manufacture, which considers making processes, materials, time factors and quality control. It also helps provide evidence of using industrial methods of manufacture.

Systems and control

Systems and control is a term used to describe how different types of systems are used to control food manufacture. These include:

- computer systems
- costing systems
- quality systems
- production systems
- safety systems (including HACCP)
- packaging and delivery systems
- marketing systems.

These different types of systems are used to control and monitor the whole manufacturing process. This enables high quality food products to be manufactured efficiently at a profit.

Systems and control is not something that you can just 'add on' to your project. You should prove its use by:

- producing a systems diagram
- developing a working schedule, including the use of a HACCP system
- using quality control.

Systems

The systems used in commercial food production involve a series of different processes working together. These processes need to be well planned in order to ensure the production of high quality products. Many commercial systems rely on the use of computers. These control the different parts of the manufacturing system. When any information is passed from one part of the system to another, this is called 'feedback'. It helps the system run more efficiently because it shows where changes might be needed to improve the process.

A recipe can be described as a system because it includes:

- an input (ingredients)
- processes (manufacturing methods)
- an output (the food product and any waste material produced during production).

The table below shows a systems diagram for making shortbread biscuits using an all-in-one method. This is a relatively simple product to make, which can be illustrated using a simple systems diagram. In this system there is no feedback, so it is called an 'open loop' system. A system that incorporates the use of feedback is called a 'closed loop' system.

Input →	Process →	Output →
• flour	• whisk ingredients in food processor	• shortbread biscuits
• butter	• shape biscuits	
• sugar	• cook	
• food processor		

'Open loop' system for shortbread biscuits

Things to do

The systems diagram shown in the table above does not include any feedback. In pairs, discuss how feedback from quality control checks at the input, process and output stages, could be used to improve the production.

Sub-systems

Large manufacturing systems are often made up of smaller sub-systems, such as marketing, research and development, stock control, production, packaging and delivery. These are all linked, through the use of computer systems, which make the whole system work together efficiently.

A systems diagram for your food product may include a number of inputs, such as ingredients, fuel, people and equipment. You may have to include a number of sub-systems, depending on the type of product you make. For example, a bread product may need to include the following sub-systems in order to achieve the output you want:

- weighing and measuring
- mixing
- proving
- shaping
- baking.

■ Things to do ■

There are many different methods for producing systems diagrams. For example, you could:

1. List all the raw materials, components, tools, equipment and processes you need in order to achieve your product output.
2. Make a table with three columns headed input, process and output. Fill in these columns with the information from your list.
3. You may need to organize parts of the three columns into vertical flow diagrams to show the sub-systems you are using.
4. Draw feedback loops at the critical control points (CCPs) to show where performance checks would take place.

Control

In industry systems are used to control all stages of manufacture, such as the amount of ingredients in a recipe (input), cooking and cooling times, oven temperatures, cutting and shaping of products (processing). All this helps to produce a successful, safe end product (output).

Control systems can be electrical, electronic, mechical or digital. They are used for:

- computer control (CAD/CAM)
- computer numerical (CNC)
- computer-integrated manufacture (CIM)
- quality control (QC)
- Hazard Analysis and Critical Control (HACCP).

Control systems incorporate feedback from sensors, switches and gauges to make sure that processes function well. Sensors can monitor oven temperatures, chilling times and temperatures, weight of individual product components, colour, pH values and moisture content. The benefits of using a control system include:

- making consistent high quality products
- making identical products efficiently
- making products to meet customer demand
- detecting faults or mistakes.

Using a control system

To produce a successful product it is important to have a series of controls within your manufacturing process to ensure the quality and consistency of the product you are making.

You can organize your control system when you produce a systems diagram. Make sure that you identify critical control points (CCPs), which show where you will undertake performance checks. Your CCPs can be at the input, processing and output stages of manufacture. For example, input checks could involve:

- visual check of ingredients for defects
- organoleptic testing of ingredients for taste and smell
- checking of weights of ingredients for accuracy
- checking of temperature of raw ingredients using probes.

Process checks could involve:

- checking oven and food temperature
- checking the safety, hygiene levels and effectiveness of each process
- checking for size, weight, colour, shape, texture and taste during manufacture
- checking of chilling times and storage methods.

Output checks could involve checking the product against specifications.

If you check for quality during the input, process and output stages of your product manufacture, it will provide you with feedback about its success. This will highlight any production problems as they occur during manufacture. You may then decide to make changes to improve your product manufacture and to reduce the possibility of wasting time, money or ingredients. Don't forget to record any changes you make.

To be successful you will need to produce an outline systems diagram for the manufacture of a product, explaining the inputs, processes, outputs and feedback. You will also need to show where performance checks are made. *(3 marks)*

Writing a schedule

You must now draw up a plan for the manufacture of your product. This plan is called a schedule. It should be easy for someone else to understand, so they could make your product exactly as you planned.

- Use your systems diagram as a starting point for your schedule so you identify the critical control points.
- Produce a step-by-step order of work, either as a work time plan, a flow diagram or a Gantt chart.
- Include the recipe with ingredients and quantities and a list of tools and equipment.
- Give details of timings during preparation and production.
- Describe the quality checks you will make at critical control points (at the input, process and output stages).
- Describe the HACCP procedures you will use at critical control points to ensure hygienic production.
- Include details of packaging and storage.
- Remember to include the scale of production.

To be successful you will need to produce a working schedule for the manufacture of a product, which considers making processes, materials, time factors and quality control. *(3 marks)*

Industrial applications

Having produced a one-off product you now need to consider how it could be adapted for manufacture on an industrial scale. For example, would you need to change or simplify any manufacturing processes? What type of equipment or machinery would be used to batch or mass produce your food product in industry?

- Compare the processes you have used with ones used in industry.
- Describe any changes to the ingredients you would use and why.
- Describe how you would scale-up your recipe.
- Could you use any standard components?
- What changes would you need to make to your schedule? Why would they be necessary?
- Describe the role that CAD/CAM would play in the manufacture of your product if it were made on a larger scale.

Scaling-up a recipe

Developing a commercial food product based on your own recipe needs careful consideration. When making a food product on a small scale, it may not matter if an extra gm of sugar or an extra ml of liquid is put in by mistake. If you repeated this on a large scale, you could have a disaster on your hands! When you scale-up your own recipe, make sure that you keep a constant ratio between the quantities of ingredients, such as fat to flour.

■ Things to do ■

1. Draw up a table to compare the ingredients used in a commercial dessert with the ingredients you would use for your own similar product.
2. Undertake sensory analysis of the commercial dessert and your own product. Report on the difference(s) in appearance, aroma, texture and taste.
3. Explain how you would adapt your own recipe ingredients for batch production.

Using standard components

If you were to manufacture your food product on a large scale you would need to consider the use of standard components. These are ready-prepared ingredients, such as flan cases, stock cubes or grated cheese. Standard components are used because they provide consistency of size, shape, flavour and quality. They can also be bought in at a known cost. For example, a pizza manufacturer may buy in grated cheese, tomato sauce and slice vegetables. This would not only save preparation time but would ensure the production of consistent and reliable end products.

■ Things to do ■

Investigate the standard components you could use to aid the manufacture of your food product. Explain the benefits they would bring.

To be successful you will need to provide clear evidence of having used appropriate industrial methods of manufacture. *(3 marks)*

5 Select and use tools, equipment and processes to make a product

This section describes how you will select and use a range of tools, equipment and processes. It helps you make a high quality product that meets the specification. It also describes how you will use safe working practices.

Select and use tools, equipment and processes

Having carefully planned the manufacture of your product, you are now ready to start making it. This is an important part of your project, as the whole section carries 36 marks, more than any of the other sections. This is an excellent opportunity for you to demonstrate your skills, knowledge and understanding of food manufacture.

Selecting and using tools, equipment and processes are worth eighteen marks. To gain the higher level marks you need to use tools, equipment and processes that require a degree of skill, for example, using a food processor, pastry making, sauce making or coating. The greater the skill required to use the equipment or the more challenging a process or technique, the greater the opportunity for you to gain marks.

Making a choice

When choosing tools, equipment and processes, you should:

- build on the experience you gained when you developed and modeled your food product.
- show how competent you have become in using tools, equipment and processes with skill and accuracy.

Remember that if you have made changes to your final design proposal, you may need to trial any new processes you intend to use.

In the food industry, a wide range of equipment is used during food production to ensure accurate and consistent results. Much of this equipment may be familiar to you, such as computerized scales, boiling vats or floor standing mixers.

Using equipment

You may not be able to use large-scale equipment, but you can often use equipment that performs similar functions, such as a food processor or digital scales. A food processor, for example, can be used for a range of different functions, similar to industrial floor standing mixers. It can knead dough, mix cakes, biscuits and pastry, process meat, vegetables or soup, all with speed, accuracy and consistency.

Your choice of tools, equipment and processes will depend on the type of food product you are making. It is vital to make a product that is challenging and that requires high level making skills, using a variety of tools and equipment. For example, making a picnic sandwich is unlikely to enable you to demonstrate your skills in the same way as making a high protein, high fibre product to be sold in a school canteen.

In order to gain as many marks as possible, you should demonstrate your ability to:

- choose the right tool for the job
- make accurate use of tools and equipment
- know how they are cared for and stored
- make competent use of processes and techniques.

Explain in your folder what tools and equipment you have chosen and why they are suitable for the job. If you come across any unexpected problems during a practical session, you may need to change or modify the processes, tools or equipment you use. Don't forget to record any changes you make in your working schedule!

To be successful you will need to select a range of appropriate tools, equipment and processes and use them with a high degree of skill and accuracy to make a product. *(18 marks)*

Making your product

The manufacture of your food product is worth eighteen marks. To gain the higher level marks you need to make a successful end product that:

- is high quality
- uses high level making skills
- makes use of computer aided manufacture (CAM) where appropriate
- is made effectively and safely
- meets all the requirements of your specification.

In order to fulfill these requirements, you should:

- work to the best of your ability
- use your working schedule to guide your practical work

- know what ingredients, quantities, tools and equipment you need
- know how to carry out all the processes in your schedule
- know your cooking times and temperatures
- evaluate the finished product against the specification.

At the end of the practical session, it is a good idea to evaluate the finished product against the specification to check it meets all the features of the design proposal. A written evaluation at this stage is very valuable. Critically analyze how you worked by evaluating:

- the good and bad points of your use of tools and equipment
- the success or failure of each process
- your product outcome – its appearance, aroma, texture and taste.

Quality issues

Quality is an important issue throughout the manufacture of your product. The product must be fit for its purpose. This can be evaluated through checking it meets user requirements, including appearance, taste and price. Fitness-for-purpose for a manufacturer means meeting the product specification and finding a balance between profitable manufacture and the needs of the user and the environment.

Make sure that you follow the quality requirements you identified in your schedule. Check quality at the critical control points you have identified. For example:

- weigh and measure your ingredients accurately
- ensure consistent chopping or mixing
- check the accuracy of timing and temperatures
- check the sensory requirements of the product.

Computer aided manufacture

In the food industry, computer aided manufacture (CAM) is used to control different processes. For example, computers can control oven temperatures, weighing and measuring, the rate at which ingredients are added, the amount of a mixture being added, the timing of processes and the speed of machinery. You should identify processes where CAM could be used in your product manufacture as a one-off and if it was batch or mass-produced.

Recording your manufacture

It is important to record in your coursework folder the different processes you have used during your product manufacture. Digital cameras are very useful for this and can also be used to photograph the finished product. Make sure that your photographs are good quality and in focus, as the examiner will need to see clear evidence of your making.

You should also record technical details, such as detailed specifications and the function of the product ingredients, together with details of the product costing. Remember to include any modifications or changes you make to the tools, equipment and processes you use. The results of quality and safety checks should also be recorded – leave a spare column for this in the appropriate place in your schedule.

To be successful you will need to make a high quality product that relates fully to the features of the design proposal. *(18 marks)*

Using safe working practices

Working safely is a requirement throughout your whole project. This means using safe working practices to ensure the safety of yourself, other people and the environment in which you work.

HACCP

Anyone who works in the food industry has a responsibility for ensuring that customers can eat their food safely. Not only must the food be safe, but also safe and hygienic working practices must be used. This is usually achieved through the use of a quality assurance system called Hazard Analysis and Critical Control (HACCP).

Managing a food production system requires the identification of anything that is a hazard (a danger) to health. A hazard is defined as something that has the potential to cause the user harm. In the food industry HACCP is used to:

- identify potential hazards
- estimate the level of risk from each hazard
- reduce or eliminate the risk.

Once possible hazards have been analyzed, critical control points are identified. These are stages in a food production system where control checks are needed to eliminate the hazard or reduce it to a safe level. HACCP therefore involves:

- looking at every stage of production
- identifying where a health hazard may occur
- deciding how to prevent the hazard, usually by using a quality control check to monitor the hazard
- checking that the quality control check is doing its job in eliminating the risk.

■ Things to do ■

Draw up a table with three columns to show:

1. Each step in making your product at the input, process and output stages.
2. The possible hazards that may occur at each stage.
3. What action is needed to reduce or eliminate the hazard?

Safety with tools, equipment and processes

Possible hazards can come from the food product itself, the environment in which you are working, the production process you use or from the tools and equipment.

Always follow your class safety rules so you make safety a high priority. Refer to the HACCP procedures you identified in your working schedule to ensure a safe and hygienic product. Remember:

- handle hot liquids with care.
- be careful with sharp tools and store them safely after use.
- dispose of waste ingredients carefully and hygienically.
- clean up spills quickly and thoroughly.

To be successful you will need to show high regard for safe working practices, recognizing the needs of both yourself and others. *(3 marks)*

6 Devise and apply tests to check the quality of the product

This section describes how you will test and check your product against the specification. It will help you evaluate the product and consider the views of users. It describes how you will use the results from evaluations to suggest and justify modifications.

Tests and checks

The aim of undertaking tests and checks is to enable you to produce a high quality product. There is a saying that 'quality cannot be manufactured into a product, but has to be *designed* into it'. This means that it is too late to wait until the manufacturing stage if you want to produce a high quality product. Quality has to be planned in right from the start so that you know when checks and tests should take place and how to check for quality.

The points when you check for quality are called critical control points (CCPs). You should have identified the CCPs in your working schedule with a description of how to check for quality. Testing and checking should therefore be recorded throughout your manufacture. You can use the findings from these tests and checks to help you evaluate your final product.

Testing against the specification

One of the most important things to remember about testing against the specification is the time factor. After your practical session you will need to evaluate the finished product against each of the specification criteria. This needs to be well organized. For example, tasting tests may need to be undertaken over more than one session, depending on the availability of users in your target market group. You may have to freeze portions of your product for testing at a later time.

You will need to devise a suitable evaluation method for each specification criteria. For example, you can undertake nutritional analysis; work out the cost of ingredients, production and packaging; evaluate your production methods; organize tasting tests with the target market group and produce questionnaires to find out their views.

Answering questions

You should aim to answer the following types of questions about your product:

- How well does the product suit the requirements of users in the target market group?
- Is it attractive and nutritious with an inviting aroma and taste?
- Is the portion size appropriate for the target market group?
- How easy is the product to prepare and eat?
- Is it suitable for batch or mass-production?
- Can it be made at a profit and sell at an attractive price?
- Does it follow food safety guidelines?
- Can the packaging be re-used? Does it store and transport the food product effectively? Does it appeal to the target market group and include appropriate information?

Make sure that you record the results of all your testing using a range of communication techniques, such as charts, star profiles or tables. The following table shows how one student used a simple checklist to record whether each specification criterion had been met.

Specification criteria	Does it meet the specification?
A nutritious, filling, savoury product that could be served in the school canteen	√
Appeal to vegetarians and meat eaters	√
Include fibre and protein and be a good source of vitamins	√
Use fresh, tasty and colourful ingredients with a variety of textures	√
Provide enough KJ/kcal per portion for a growing teenager	X
Cost between 70–90p per portion	X
Be suitable for small batch production	√
Suitable for freezing with a shelf life of three months	√
Use a heat resistant food container that can be recycled	X

Nutritional analysis

Nutritional analysis is a way of evaluating the nutritional content of a food product. This can then be checked against the specification criteria. If you are producing food for a diabetic, you will have to calculate the sugar content. Other consumer groups also have special nutritional requirements. For example, teenagers need a balanced diet that provides specific energy requirements.

Although food labeling regulations require certain information on food products, it is not a legal requirement to include nutritional information. However, many manufacturers do provide this type of information since many consumers find it useful. It also backs up a manufacturer's claim that a product is 'low fat', has 'reduced sugar' or is 'high in fibre'.

When you calculate the nutritional content of your food product, you may need to work out nutritional information for the whole dish and a single portion. Include this information on the food label.

Nutritional analysis may involve calculating the energy value and the amount of protein, fat, carbohydrate and fibre in each portion. After evaluating the results against your specification criteria, you may have to modify your recipe. For example, you could:

- reduce the sugar content
- reduce the salt content by adding spices instead of salt
- increase the fibre by adding peas or beans
- reduce the fat content by reducing the amount of cheese or bacon.

▪ Things to do ▪

1. Investigate the labeling requirements for processed foods, such as dried or tinned foods.
2. Calculate the nutritional content of your food product using a nutritional analysis software program or spreadsheet.

Working out costs

Food product costs in industry include the cost of ingredients, labour, production, packaging and distribution. The costing must produce an accurate price that will make the product saleable and produce a profit – both for the manufacturer and the retailer.

Costing includes:

- direct costs like ingredients, labour and packaging
- overhead costs like rent, electricity, water, distribution and marketing.

Some manufacturers work out overhead costs as a percentage of direct costs. For example, if direct costs were 90p per portion, then they may add a further 30 per cent for overheads, making the manufacturing costs £1.17. The retailer may add up to 40 per cent to make the price in the shop around £1.64 per portion. However the costs are calculated, the price must provide 'value for money' for the consumer.

▪ Things to do ▪

1. Work out the cost of ingredients for your product per portion. Add ten per cent for labour and packaging to find the direct costs.
2. Add 30 per cent for overheads to find you manufacturing costs per portion. How much would the product sell for in the shops?

To be successful you will need to develop and use appropriate testing techniques to check the product against all aspects of the specification.

(3 marks)

Evaluating your product

Your final product evaluation should bring together the results of all your tests and checks. You should make use of:

- the checks you made during the manufacture
- the tests you made against the specification criteria
- the views of users in your target market group.

Make sure that you fully explain and justify how your product has met (or not met) the specification criteria. You should also comment on how well you used your time during the project, including any unforeseen problems you had and how you overcame them. (These should have been recorded in your working schedule.)

Target market group views

Finding out the views of users is relatively easy if your product is aimed at teenagers in your own age group. If the product is for children or for vegetarians, for example, it can be more difficult. You may have to organize tasting tests either in school or at another location, such as a playgroup. Check with your teacher, if necessary, to see how you could organize this kind of activity.

Don't forget that any comments from the target market group should be objective. This means that they should be made against the specification criteria, rather than just being personal opinion. Comments such as 'I don't like the taste' are meaningless unless they are justified with reasons why the taste is not liked.

Writing a questionnaire

Writing a questionnaire, based on the specification criteria, is a good way to target the answers you want to find out. You could ask users to fill in a questionnaire at a product tasting session.

There are two types of questionnaire – open and closed. Try not to ask questions, such as 'Why do you think this product is successful?' This type of question would result in many different types of answers, which may not be very helpful. It is better to ask closed questions, which can be based on the specification criteria. For example, you could ask users to rate out of five the appearance, aroma, texture and taste of your product.

■ Things to do ■

Design a questionnaire to find out the views of your target market group about your product. Ask a closed question about each of your specification criteria.

To be successful you will need to evaluate the final product, using evidence from test results and considering the users' views. *(3 marks)*

All the testing and evaluation you undertake will provide you with feedback about the success of your product. This should provide you with enough information for you to suggest modifications to improve the performance of your product. This might take the form of modifications to:

- the product design – to meet more closely the needs of the target market group.
- the ingredients – could you use standard components to reduce costs?
- the manufacturing process – to make the product more cost-effective to manufacture.
- the scale of production – to manufacture the product in a higher volume.
- the target market group – is the product more suited to a different age group, for example?

Remember to record any modifications in the evaluation section of your design folder. Explain why and how they will improve the performance of your product. It is also appropriate at this point to include your views about what you would do differently if you did the project again, or if you feel that you put enough effort into your work.

To be successful you will need to use the results from evaluations to suggest and justify modifications. *(3 marks)*

Coursework tips and hints

Project management

- Discuss the coursework deadlines with your teacher, so you know how much time is available for your coursework.
- Take *some* responsibility for planning, organizing, managing and evaluating your own project.
- Use similar headings to the assessment criteria for writing up your work.
- Make sure that you have clear photographs to show your manufacturing processes.
- Make sure that you have clear photographs to show your final product.

How to make sure your coursework project is a success

- Discuss your project with your teacher to make sure it is appropriate.
- Check out how many marks are awarded for each of the assessment criteria. The more marks that are available, the more work you will need to do in order to achieve them.
- Be very selective in what you research. Only use the information that helps you make decisions about what to design and make.
- Develop a specification based on your research.
- Use your specification to generate outline ideas. Evaluate your ideas against the specification.
- Develop, model and test your ideas, until you develop a realistic design proposal.
- Use a variety of communication techniques, including the use of ICT where appropriate.
- Producing a systems diagram and a working schedule for one-off production and for industrial manufacture.
- Use specialist and technical language.
- Select and use tools, equipment and processes with skill and accuracy.
- Make a high quality product that matches the design proposal.
- Evaluate your product against the specification to test its fitness-for-purpose.
- Use feedback from testing to suggest modifications to your product.
- Write up your project as you go, using word processing if possible. This will enable you to edit and change your work as it develops.

Submitting your coursework folder

- Finish your project in time for you teacher to send your folder to the examiner by 1 May in Year 11.
- Attach the Candidate Mark Record sheet on the front page of your folder.
- Attach photographs of your product to the front page.
- Write your Product Title, centre number, candidate name and number on the front page of your folder.
- Write your centre number, candidate name and number on all the other pages.
- Number your pages, then add a contents page.
- Make sure that your work is clear and easy to understand.

Short-course coursework

What to expect

- You can choose a set task from a list of project briefs or develop a project idea based on a topic set by your teacher.
- You will be expected to produce a food product and a ten page A3 design folder.
- You should spend up to 20 hours on your project. Check with your teacher to see how many lessons you will have over how many weeks. Knowing how much time is available will help you plan and organize your project successfully.

How will it be assessed?

- The coursework project accounts for 60 per cent of the marks for the short-course.
- Your project is assessed using the designing and making criteria shown in the table opposite, *Short-course assessment criteria*.

Designing and manufacturing

During your course, you will be asked to analyze commercial products to see how they are designed and manufactured. Analyzing products will help you understand issues related to user needs and moral, cultural and environmental issues. Product analysis is therefore a very useful activity because it can develop your understanding of the design and manufacture of high quality products.

When you undertake coursework, the designing process will help you develop:

- skills of problem solving, including moral, cultural and environmental issues.
- communication techniques using a variety of media, including the use of ICT.

When you undertake coursework, the making process will help you:

- explore and practise a variety of manufacturing techniques.
- be imaginative and experimental when combining materials.
- use CAD/CAM where appropriate and available.
- demonstrate your understanding of industrial practices.

	Assessment criteria	Marks
1	Use information sources to develop detailed specifications	6
2	Develop ideas from the specification	24
3	Use written communication and graphical techniques	6
4	Produce and use a detailed working schedule	6
5	Select and use tools, equipment and processes to make a product	36
6	Devise and apply tests to check the quality of the product	6
	Total marks	84

Short-course assessment criteria

Coursework project design folder

Your design folder should be concise and only include information that is really relevant to your project. This means that you will need to be very selective about what to include so that you can target the available marks. Your folder should be produced on approximately ten proforma A3 pages, provided by your teacher. You should treat each of the ten proforma pages as design exercises in themselves so you include as much relevant information as possible in the space available. You will be allowed **one** supplementary page if necessary.

Using the coursework section

The following short-course section will take you through the assessment criteria, describing how to achieve the best marks.

1 Use information sources to develop detailed specifications

This section describes how you will select and use information from a wide range of sources. It will help you produce a design specification for your product.

Where do I start?

Your teacher may ask you to develop a project idea based on a set topic or suggest that you select from a list of set tasks. Making decisions at the start of a project is always very difficult, so discuss your project idea with your teacher to make sure that it will allow you to gain as many marks as possible from the assessment criteria.

Designing for people

Although new food products are developed for all sorts of different reasons, remember that they are designed for people. This means taking into account the needs and values of potential users for your product – finding out about the kind of food they already eat and their likes and dislikes. As a designer, you must be very clear about who you are designing for – your target market group.

Working in a team is an ideal way to explore ideas about your target market group. It can provide just the support you need to get going. You could try brainstorming:

- the kind of target market group you could design for – are they vegetarians, young children or busy students?
- the kind of food products they like to eat.

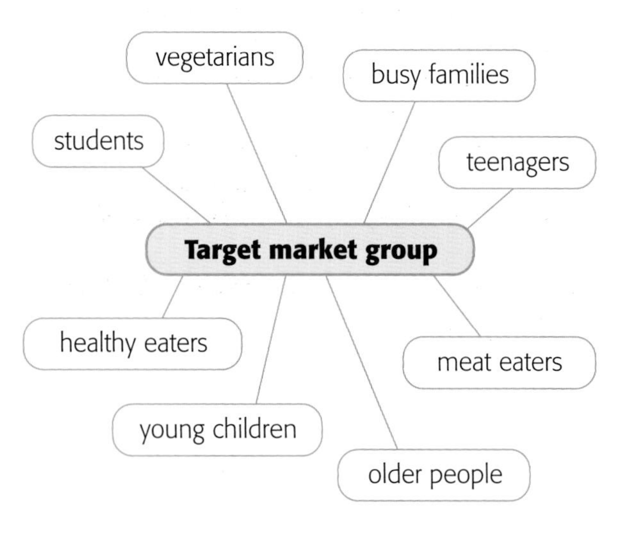

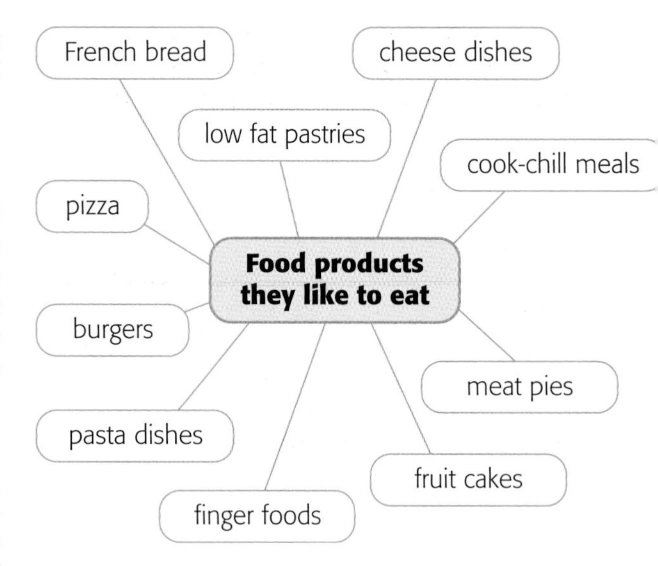

Brainstorming user and market needs

Whatever starting point for your project, you will need to ask questions about the need for the food product you intend to design and make. For example:

- What are the needs of users of the product? For example, their age range, food needs, leisure activities and lifestyle.
- What kind of food product would satisfy the needs of these users? What level of nutrition should the product provide?
- What kind of similar food products are there already on the market? How much do they cost?
- In what situation would the product be eaten? For example, is it a family dish, for picnics or for school dinners?
- What are the latest trends in eating? Is pasta still popular or are organic foods gaining ground?

Developing a design brief

Asking questions about your product idea and potential users in your target market group should help you to write a design brief and plan your research. Your design brief needs to be simple and concise and should explain:

- what needs to be designed (a new kind of dessert? A main course rice dish?)
- who it is for (vegans or students?)
- any special user requirements (nutritional, cultural, religious or economic?)
- the benefits it will bring the users (easy to eat on the move? Easy to prepare?)

Your design brief is very important because it will help you pinpoint the information you need to collect in order to design and develop your product idea.

Design brief

Design and make a low cost savoury main dish for the school canteen. The product should be suitable for vegetarians and easy to prepare.

Your design brief should guide your research

Gathering information

You will need to gather relevant information from a wide range of appropriate sources. You only have ten pages for the whole project and just one page to:

- list your sources of information
- summarize the most useful information you find
- write your design specification.

The key to success is to be very selective in what you research and to only use information that can really help you make decisions about what you are going to design and make. You may wish to consider some of the following sources of information:

- market research – a shop survey of similar existing food products
- a consumer survey – a questionnaire to find out the needs of your target market group
- product analysis – to find out about the design, manufacture, target market group and price range of a similar existing food products
- a visit to a manufacturer – possibly using the Internet, videos or a CD ROM
- a product test report – such as *Which* magazine or from the Good Housekeeping Institute
- a database or CD ROM to find out about nutritional information
- leaflets from supermarkets and information from textbooks.

You do not have to use all these information sources, but do try to use those that are most helpful. Three different sources should provide you with enough information to write a design specification.

Remember you only have 20 hours for your project, which may limit some kinds of research you can do. For example, it is not always possible to write off to companies and get useful information back in time.

To be successful you will need to select and use information from a wide range of appropriate sources. *(3 marks)*

Producing a specification

Once you have summarized your research information, you are ready to write a design specification. This should give details of the product's form, function and budgetary constraints. In other words, your food specification should describe:

- the product type and its purpose
- the requirements of the target market group
- nutritional information
- the type of ingredients to be used
- the portion size
- the price range of the product
- the scale of production
- safety factors, such as the expected shelf life of the product
- environmental issues.

Your design specification should give you a clear structure to work to and should guide your thinking about the food product you are developing. You should refer to your specification criteria when evaluating your design ideas.

To be successful you will need to produce a specification that describes form, function, user requirements and budgetary constraints. *(3 marks)*

Specification

My food product must:

- be a nutritious, filling, savoury product that could be served in the school canteen.
- appeal to vegetarians and meat eaters.
- include fibre and protein and be a good source of vitamins.
- use fresh, tasty and colourful ingredients, with a variety of textures.
- provide enough kj/kcal per portion for a growing teenager
- cost between 70-90p per portion.
- be suitable for small batch production.
- suitable for freezing with a shelf life of three months.
- use a heat resistant food container that can be recycled.

2 Develop ideas from the specification

This section describes how you will present a range of realistic and imaginative design ideas based on your specification. You will then develop, model and test your design ideas to produce a realistic design proposal.

Generating ideas

Generating a range of realistic and imaginative ideas is worth up to twelve marks, so it is really something that you can get your teeth into! It gives you the opportunity to display your creativity and design abilities.

Realistic ideas are ones that can be designed and made in the time available to you. You only have 20 hours for the whole project, which means that you need to be very focused on what you have to do. Look for suitable dishes or recipes that you can develop to meet the requirements of your specification. Recipe books, magazines and any menu planning software you may have access to will all be helpful in generating ideas.

You need to present at least three alternative ideas, so choose products that use different materials, processes and working techniques. Be imaginative, don't just settle for dishes you have cooked before, but choose dishes that demand a high level of practical skill.

Presenting your ideas

Clearly present your ideas, using simple labeled diagrams or pictures of the food product. Explain why and how your ideas meet the requirements of the target market group. This can be done by evaluating each of your outline food product ideas against your specification criteria. You could compile your results in a table, such as the one opposite.

To be successful you will need to present a range of realistic and imaginative design ideas that address the specification. *(12 marks)*

Developing modelling ideas

Having evaluated your outline ideas you now need to develop them further. This section is worth up to twelve marks, so it is worthwhile thinking them through fully. Check your ideas with your teacher, so you know you are working at a level that will enable you to gain the most marks.

Specification criteria	Idea 1	Idea 2	Idea 3
Nutritious, filling, savoury product	√	√	√
Suit vegetarians and meat eaters	√	X	√
Include fibre, protein and vitamins	X	√	√
Tasty, colourful and textured	√	√	√
KJ/kcal per portion for growing teenager	X	√	X
70–90p per portion	√	√	X
Suitable for small batch production	√	√	√
Freezable with three month shelf life	√	√	X
Recyclable heat- resistant container	√	√	√

Evaluating food product ideas

You can model your ideas by trialling the production of each dish. Your trial production should include details of:

- ingredients and quantities
- tools and equipment
- the method of making, with timings
- HACCP
- quality checks.

Remember to make a note of any problems that occur when you model your product ideas. If you have the opportunity to take photographs of your product modelling, this will not only provide evidence of your work in your folder, but will give you a reference point for further development.

Testing ideas against the specification

Testing is a very important part of your product development. Compare each of your food products against the specification criteria. This may involve the use of comparative tests, setting up a tasting panel or using sensory analysis tests. This type of testing involves the use of sensory descriptors, such as appearance, aroma, texture and taste. Comparative testing can either make use of a random sample of people or, more usefully, a sample from your target market group. Remember to record the results of your testing using a star profile, hedonic rating or a tasting chart.

The final design proposal

Testing your design ideas should provide you with enough information to develop your final design proposal. You may need to:

- combine the best aspects of each idea to produce the best solution
- modify your ideas and repeat the trialling and testing processes.

You should clearly record on 'The Chosen Design' sheet your final design proposal, together with details of tests, modifications, the final specification and reasons for your product choice.

To be successful you will need to develop, model and test design ideas to produe a realistic design proposal. *(12 marks)*

3 Use written communication and graphical techniques

In this section marks will be awarded for clear written communication, using specialist vocabulary. You will use graphical techniques, other media and ICT with skill and accuracy.

To be successful you will need to clearly communicate information in a logical way and well organized manner, using appropriate specialist vocabulary. *(3 marks)*

Written communication

The marks for written communication can be picked up throughout your design folder. You should aim to use specialist and technical language related to food technology in all the writing that you do. Your use of specialist language must be accurate and your writing clearly presented, with information set out in a logical way.

For example, one student used the following language to describe a biological aspect of her work:

Before the biscuit dough is mixed, the starch and protein molecules in the flour are separated. During mixing, the protein molecules unfold and link around the starch molecules and the protein strands form a matrix or network. The linked protein molecules are elastic and allow the dough to stretch.

What you write reflects your knowledge and understanding about food technology. High quality writing should form the basis of your design folder. For example, your design brief, specification and the evaluation of your ideas will be written. When you annotate your design ideas, report on product testing or produce a working schedule, you will have the opportunity to demonstrate your understanding of specialist technical terms and identify specific materials and manufacturing processes.

Your folder work can be either hand or computer generated. You will be given credit for high quality work whichever way you produce it – either by hand or using computer software.

Other media and ICT

Good quality communication skills are essential if you are to demonstrate your product ideas, knowledge and understanding to others, including the examiner. There are many different ways of communicating ideas other than simply writing. For example, you could use any of the following techniques and media:

- Graphical techniques, for example, bar charts, pie charts or star profiles.
- Brainstorms, for example, in the form of a spider diagram.
- Tables, for example, nutritional analysis tables, costings, tables showing HACCP and quality control points.
- Flow diagrams, for example, to show manufacturing processes and the order of assembly.
- Photographs, using either film or digital methods.
- Cut and past from magazines, for example, developing ideas or packaging ideas.
- Sketching by hand, for example, for products, packaging or labelling.

Using ICT

You may have the opportunity to use ICT to enhance your food technology work. You should provide evidence of your use of ICT in your coursework folder, although you will not lose marks if you produce work by hand.

Software programs are very useful for word processing because they enable you to write text, design questionnaires, edit, change and save your work. Other types of software can be used to help with the presentation of your work, for costing, nutritional analysis and for producing labeling for your product. Look out for opportunities to use ICT in any of the following activities.

Research

- Use a database or CD ROM to search for nutritional information.
- Use the Internet to find information about nutrition and health, food materials, existing products and lifestyles.
- Use survey software or a DTP package to generate questionnaires and results.
- Use a spreadsheet to analyze research information. This makes it easy to produce charts, diagrams or graphs to present the results of research.

Presenting ideas and planning manufacture

- Use a digital camera or scanned images to produce sources for ideas.
- Use specialist software for nutritional analysis.
- Use a CAD package to produce images of food, to produce templates for cutting or for packaging design.
- Use food modelling software to produce 'virtual' 3D products.
- Use a spreadsheet to cost a product, calculate production in quantity, to analyze the results of comparative tests, tasting tests or sensory analysis.
- Use HACCP software simulation to plan risk assessment.
- Use computer-generated flowcharts to plan manufacture.

Product manufacture

- Use CAM to make food of repeatable quality, such as using a bread maker for identical loaves.
- Use a digital camera to record the sequence of making and testing your project.

Presenting your work

You must present your work to the best of your ability. Take time to plan the layout of each page since you only have ten pages in all to present your work.

- Check the accuracy of tables and charts and make sure they are clearly labeled, so the examiner understands your intentions.
- Sketches or diagrams of food products or packaging should include measurements if they are relevant to the product.
- Make sure that you take time to set up photographs, so your food product is shown to its best advantage.
- Check that photographs are in focus.
- Digital images should be printed on high quality paper.

To be successful you will need to use graphical techniques, photographs, cut-outs, models and mock-ups appropriately with a high degree of skill and accuracy. *(3 marks)*

4 Produce and use a detailed working schedule

This section describes how to produce a systems diagram, showing inputs, processes, outputs and feedback. It helps you write a working schedule for your product manufacture that shows where performance checks are made. It also helps you provide evidence of using industrial methods of manufacture during making.

Systems and control

Systems and control is not something that you can just 'add on' to your project. You should evidence its use by:

- producing a systems diagram
- developing a working schedule, including the use of a HACCP system
- using quality control.

Systems

The systems used in commercial food production involve a series of different processes working together.

- These processes need to be well planned in order to ensure the production of high quality products.
- Many commercial systems rely on the use of computers. These control the different parts of the manufacturing system.
- When any information is passed from one part of the system to another, this is called 'feedback'. It helps the system run more efficiently because it shows where changes might be needed to improve the process.

A recipe can be described as a system because it includes an input (ingredients), processes (manufacturing methods) and an output (the food product). The table below shows a systems diagram for making shortbread biscuits, using an all-in-one method. This is a relatively simple product to make, which can be illustrated using a simple systems diagram.

Input →	Process →	Output →
• flour	• whisk ingredients in food processor	• shortbread biscuits
• butter	• shape biscuits	
• sugar	• cook	
• food processor		

Systems diagram for shortbread biscuits

However, a systems diagram for your food product may be more complex. You may need more inputs and more processes to achieve your product output.

Control

When you produce a systems diagram for your product manufacture, make sure that you identify critical control points (CCPs), where you will undertake performance checks. Your CCPs can be at the input, processing and output stages of manufacture. For example, input checks could involve:

- visual checks of ingredients for defects
- organoleptic testing of ingredients for taste and smell
- weighing of ingredients for accuracy
- temperature checks of raw ingredients.

Process checks could involve:

- checking the safety, hygiene levels and effectiveness of each process
- checking for size, weight, colour, shape, texture and taste during manufacture.

Output checks could involve checking the product against specifications.

If you check for quality during the input, process and output stages of your product manufacture, it will provide you with feedback about its success. You may then decide to make changes to improve your product manufacture. Remember to record any changes you make.

Writing a schedule

The plan for manufacture of your product is called a schedule. It should be easy for someone else to understand, so they could make your product exactly as you planned.

- Use your systems diagram as a starting point for writing your schedule, so you identify the critical control points.
- Produce a step-by-step order of work, either as a work time plan or as a flow diagram.
- Include the recipe, quantities, a list of equipment, details of timings during preparation and production.
- Describe the quality checks you will make at critical control points (at the input, process and output stages).
- Describe the HACCP procedures you will follow at critical control points to ensure safe and hygienic production.
- Include details of packaging and storage.

To be successful you will need to produce an outline systems diagram for the manufacture of a product, showing inputs, processes, outputs and feedback. You will need to write a detailed working schedule for manufacture and show where checks are made. *(3 marks)*

Industrial applications

Having produced a one-off product you now need to consider how it could be manufactured on an industrial scale. For example, would you need to change or simplify any manufacturing processes? What type of equipment or machinery would be used to batch or mass produce your food product in industry?

- Compare the processes you have used with ones used in industry.
- Describe any changes to the ingredients you would use and why.
- What changes would you need to make to your schedule? Why would they be necessary?
- Describe the role that CAD/CAM would play in the manufacture of your product if it was made on a large scale.

To be successful you will need to provide clear evidence of having used industrial methods of manufacture to some advantage during making. *(3 marks)*

5 Select and use tools, equipment and processes to make a product

This section describes how you will select a range of tools, equipment and processes and use them safely. It helps you make a high quality product that meets the specification.

To be successful you will need to select a range of appropriate tools, equipment and processes and use them with a high degree of skill and accuracy to make a product safely. *(18 marks)*

Select and use tools, equipment and processes

Having carefully planned the manufacture of your product, you are now ready to start making it. This is an important part of your project as the whole section carries 36 marks, more than any of the other sections. Selecting and using tools, equipment and processes is worth eighteen marks. This is an excellent opportunity for you to demonstrate your skills, knowledge and understanding of food manufacture.

Making a choice

When choosing tools, equipment and processes, you should build on the experience you gained when you developed and modeled your food product. Show how competent you have become in using tools, equipment and processes with skill and accuracy. In the food industry a wide range of equipment is used during food production to ensure accurate and consistent results. Much of this equipment may be familiar to you, such as computerized scales, boiling vats or floor standing mixers.

Your choice of tools, equipment and processes will depend on the type of food product you are making. It is vital to make a product that is challenging and that requires high level making skills, using a variety of tools and equipment. For example, making a picnic sandwich is unlikely to enable you to demonstrate your skills in the same way as making a high protein, high fibre product to be sold in a school canteen.

In order to gain as many marks as possible, you should demonstrate your ability to:

- make accurate use of tools and equipment
- make competent use of processes and techniques
- follow your class safety rules and use the HACCP procedures you identified in your working schedule to ensure a safe and hygienic product.

If you come across any unexpected problems during a practical session, you may need to change or modify the processes, tools or equipment you use. Don't forget to record any changes you make in your working schedule!

Making your product

Making a food product is worth eighteen marks. In order to gain as many marks as possible, you should make a product that:

- is high quality
- uses high level making skills
- makes use of computer aided manufacture (CAM) where appropriate
- is made effectively and safely
- meets all the requirements of your specification.

In order to fulfill these requirements, you should:

- work to the best of your ability
- use your working schedule to guide your practical work
- know what ingredients, quantities, tools and equipment you need
- know how to carry out all the processes in your schedule
- know your cooking times and temperatures
- evaluate the finished product against the specification.

Quality issues

Quality is an important issue throughout the manufacture of your product. Make sure that you follow the quality requirements in your schedule. Check quality at the critical control points you have identified. For example, weigh and measure your ingredients accurately, ensure consistent chopping or mixing, check the accuracy of timing and temperatures and check the sensory requirements of the product.

Computer aided manufacture

In the food industry computer aided manufacture (CAM) is used to control different processes. For example, computers can control oven temperatures, weighing and measuring the rate at which ingredients are added, the amount of a mixture being used, the timing of processes and the speed of machinery. You should identify processes where CAM could be used in your product manufacture and if it was batch or mass produced.

Recording your manufacture

It is important to record in your coursework folder the different processes you have used during your product manufacture. Digital cameras are very useful for this and can also be used to photograph the finished product. Make sure that your photographs are good quality and in focus, as the examiner will need to see evidence of your making.

You should also record in your working schedule any modifications or changes you make to the tools, equipment and processes you use. The results of quality and safety checks should also be recorded – leave a spare column for this in the appropriate place in your schedule.

To be successful you will need to make a high quality product that relates fully to the features of the design proposal. *(18 marks)*

6 Devise and apply tests to check the quality of the product

This section describes how you will test and check your product against the specification. It will help you evaluate the final product, consider the views of users and suggest modifications.

Tests and checks

The aim of undertaking tests and checks is to produce a high quality product. There is a saying that 'quality cannot be manufactured into a product, but has to be designed into it'. This means that it is too late to wait until the manufacturing stage if you want to produce a high quality product. Quality has to be planned in right from the start, so that you know when checks and tests should take place and how to check for quality.

The points when you check for quality are called critical control points (CCPs). You should have identified the CCPs in your working schedule with a description of how to check for quality. Testing and checking should therefore be recorded throughout your product manufacture. You can use the findings from these tests and checks to help you evaluate your final product.

Testing against the specification

One of the most important things to remember about testing against the specification is the time factor. After your practical session, you will need to evaluate the finished product against each of the specification criteria. This needs to be well organized. For example, tasting tests may need to be undertaken over more than one session, depending on the availability of users in your target market group. You may have to freeze portions of your product for testing at a later time.

You will need to devise a suitable evaluation method for each specification criteria. For example, you can undertake nutritional analysis; work out the cost of ingredients, production and packaging; evaluate your production methods; organize tasting tests with the target market group and produce questionnaires to find out their views.

You should aim to answer the following types of questions about your product:

- How well does the product suit the requirements of users in the target market group?
- Is it attractive and nutritious, with an inviting aroma and taste?
- How easy is the product to prepare and eat?
- Is it suitable for batch or mass production?
- Can it be made at a profit and sell at an attractive price?
- Does it follow food safety guidelines?
- Can the packaging be re-used?

Make sure that you record the results of all your testing using a range of communication techniques, such as charts, star profiles or tables.

To be successful you will need to develop and use appropriate testing techniques to check the product against all aspects of the specification. *(3 marks)*

Evaluating your product

Your final product evaluation should bring together the results of all your tests and checks. You should make use of:

- the checks you made during manufacture
- the test you made against the specification criteria
- the views of users in your target market group.

Make sure that you fully explain and justify how your product has met each of the specification criteria. You should also comment on how well you used your time during the project, including any unforeseen problems you had and how you overcame them. (These should have been recorded in your working schedule.)

Target market group views

Finding out the views of users is relatively easy if your product is aimed at teenagers in your own age group. If the product is for children or for vegetarians, however, it can be more difficult. You may have to organize tasting tests either in school or at another location, such as a playgroup. Check with your teacher, if necessary, to see how you could organize this kind of activity.

Remember that any comments from the target market group should be objective. This means that they should be made against the specification criteria, rather than being just personal opinion. Comments such as 'I don't like the taste' are meaningless, unless they are justified with reason why the taste is not liked. Writing a questionnaire, based on the specification criteria, is a good way to target the answer you want to find out. It is better to ask 'closed' questions, which aim to find out specific answers. For example, you could ask users to rate out of 5 the appearance, aroma, texture and taste of your product.

Suggest modifications

All the testing and evaluation you undertake will provide you with feedback about the success of your product. It will enable you to explain and justify its fitness-for-purpose against the specification criteria.

You should now be in a position to suggest modifications to improve the performance of your product. This might take the form of modifications to:

- the product design
- the ingredients, including the use of standard components
- the manufacturing processes
- the scale of production
- the target market.

It is also appropriate at this point to include your views about what you would do differently if you did the project again or if you feel that you put enough effort into your work.

To be successful you will need to evaluate the final product, using evidence from test results and the views of users. You will need to suggest and justify modifications. *(3 marks)*

Coursework tips and hints

Project management

- Discuss the coursework deadlines with your teacher, so you know how much time is available for your coursework.
- Take some responsibility for planning, organizing, managing and evaluating your own project.
- Use the ten page A3 Coursework Folio to guide the content of your design folder.
- Make sure that you have clear photographs to show your manufacturing processes.
- Make sure that you have clear photographs to show your final product.

How to make sure your coursework project is a success

- Discuss your project with your teacher to make sure it is appropriate.
- Check out how many marks are awarded for each of the assessment criteria. The more marks that are available, the more work you will need to do to achieve them.
- Be very selective in what you research. Only use information that helps you make decisions about what to design and make.
- Develop a specification based on your research.
- Use your specification to generate outline ideas. Evaluate your ideas against the specification.
- Develop, model and test your ideas, until you develop a realistic design proposal.
- Use a variety of communication techniques, including the use of ICT where appropriate.
- Producing a systems diagram and a working schedule for the manufacture of the product.
- Use specialist and technical language.
- Consider how to manufacture your product on an industrial scale.
- Select and use tools, equipment and processes with skill and accuracy.
- Make a high quality product that matches the design proposal.
- Evaluate your product against the specification to test its fitness-for-purpose.
- Use feedback from testing to suggest modifications to your product.

Submitting your coursework folder

- Finish your project in time for your teacher to send it to the examiner by 1 May in Year 11.
- Attach the Candidate Mark Record sheet on the front page of your folder.
- Write your Brief Number, Product Title, centre number, candidate name and number on the front page of your folder.
- Write your centre number, candidate name and number on every other page.
- Make sure that your work is clear and easy to understand.

Further information and useful addresses

Useful Internet sites

- www.nutrition.org.uk
- www.maff.gov.uk
- http://seafish.co.uk
- www.bakersfederation.org.uk
- www.britishsugar.co.uk
- www.cadbury.co.uk
- www.foodfuture.org.uk
- www.mcdonalds.com
- www.britishmeat.org.uk
- www.milk.co.uk
- www.ndc.co.uk
- www.healthnet.org.uk
- www.nutsoc.org.uk
- www.veg.org/veg

Useful addresses

Alliance for Beverage Cartons and the Environment
24–28 Bloomsbury Way
London
WC1A 2PX

British Egg Information Service
Bury House
126–128 Cromwell Road
London
SW7 5ET

Cadbury Ltd
External Services Department
PO Box 12
Bournville
Birmingham
B30 2LU

The Flour Advisory Bureau
21 Arlington Street
London
SW1A 1RN

Food and Drink Federation
Education Service
6 St Catherine Street
London
WC2B 5JJ

Kellogg Co. of Great Britain
Kellogg Building
Talbot Road
Manchester
M16 0PU

MAFF Food Sense Booklets
Food Sense
London
SE99 7TT

National Dairy Council
5–7 John Princes Street
London
W1M 0AP

British Nutrition Foundation
High Holborn House
52–53 High Holborn
London
WC1V 6RU

The Food Commission (UK)
5–11 Warship Street
London
EC2A 2BH

Meat and Livestock Commission
PO Box 44
Winterhill House
Snowdon Drive
Milton Keynes
MK6 1AX

The Packaging Federation
Nottingham Road
Melton Mowbray
Leicestershire
LE13 0NU

The Vegan Society
7 Battle Road
St Leonards-on-sea
East Sussex
TN37 7AA

The Vegetarian Society
Parkdale
Durnham Road
Altrincham
Cheshire
WA14 4QG

Data
16 Wellesbourne House
Walton Road
Wellesbourne
Warwicks
CV35 9JB

Glossary

additives natural or synthetic substances added to foods in small amounts to preserve them, flavour them, or enhance colour, texture and so on

aeration incorporating air into a mixture, for example, beating egg whites will aerate them

AFD accelerated freeze drying – a method of drying frozen foods in a vacuum

ambient temperature room temperature

anaemia shortage of red blood cells, causing weakness and paling of the skin

artificial sweeteners used to provide the sweetness, but not the energy value of sugar

bacteria micro-organisms, some of which may be harmful and contaminate foods

bacterial culture the growing of bacteria on a special food and in carefully controlled conditions

batch production a specific quantity of the same product produced in a single production run

CAD Computer Aided Design

CAM Computer Aided Manufacture

caramelization the process of heating sugar above melting point to produce caramel. This can be added to foods to produce colour and flavour

cholesterol fat made naturally by the body. The body needs some cholesterol, but too much can cause heart disease

CIM Computer Integrated Manufacture

CNC Computer Numerical Control

coeliacs a disease some people suffer from, which is an intolerance of gluten – the protein found in wheat, barley, rye, oats and in products made from these grains

competitive advantage those things that the food producer can do better than its competitors

components ready-prepared ingredients bought in by manufacturers to assemble into finished food products, for example, pizza bases

composites ready-made components that need further processing to become food products, for example, stock cubes and dried soup mixes

critical control point (CCP) a point in the production process where a hazard might occur, therefore, also a point at which actin must be taken to monitor, reduce or eliminate the hazard

cross-contamination the transfer of bacteria or other contaminants from one production area to another, or from one food to another

Dietary Reference Values (DRVs) estimates of the amount of nutrients needed by different groups of people

disassembly taking a food product apart in order to find out what it is made from, its nutritional value and its construction

enzyme chemicals produced by living cells. There are lots of different enzymes. Some react with food ingredients, for example, some bacteria produce enzymes that cause food to rot

Estimated Average Requirement (EARs) estimated requirements that show specific needs of individuals may vary

extrinsic sugars you can see, for example, icing sugar and granulated sugar

extruded to force a mixture through a die or nozzle at great pressure, for example, piped biscuit mixture

feedback collecting data and passing this back to a central control unit. Feedback is used in CAM systems to monitor production processes

fibre see **non-starch polysaccharides (NSP)**

flow chart a chart showing the sequence of stages in the design and making of a food product

fortified enriched, particularly in the case of adding vitamins and minerals to a food product

HACCP Hazard Analysis and Critical Control Points

high biological value (HBV) proteins which contain all the essential amino acids

high-risk area the part of the food production area where there is a risk of bacterial contamination of food ingredients and products. Food must never move from a high-risk area to a low-risk area

high-risk foods foods which are liable to bacterial contamination, for example, yoghurt

input food, material or information at the start of a system, for example, the input at the start of yoghurt production is fresh milk

intrinsic invisible sugars, for example, those that occur naturally in fruit and vegetables

iron a mineral needed by the body to keep blood cells healthy. Vitamin C helps the body to absorb iron

low biological value (LBV) proteins that lack one or more of the essential amino acids

low-risk area the part of the food production area where there is little chance of the bacterial contamination of food

micro-organisms any small organism that can only be seen with a microscope

modelling testing, developing and predicting ideas and outcomes, often using computers, for example, computer programmes can model the nutritional value of food

monounsaturated fats found in vegetables and nuts

moulding forming a food product into a particular shape, for example, producing round scones and beef burgers

non-starch polysaccharides (NSP) also know as fibre. It is found in the cell walls of plants. Pectin is a NSP, which is soluble in water, and bran is a NSP, which is not soluble in water

nutrients substances found in foods we eat, for example, carbohydrates, minerals and so on

output the finished product or the final result of a system, for example, the output of a brewery is a beer

pasteurization a heat treatment which destroys most bacteria and other micro-organisms. Milk is pasteurized by heating it to 72°C for at least 15 seconds and then cooling it rapidly to 10°C

pathogenic harmful

pH level acidity is measured on the pH scale. pH 7.0 is neutral (neither acid nor alkaline), substances which are very acidic will have a low number on the scale and substances, which are alkaline, will have a high number on the scale

polyunsaturated fats found in nuts, grains, seeds and oily fish

primary processing processing raw food ingredients, for example, milling wheat to make flour

product profile the criteria a product must satisfy to meet the needs of the target market group. A description of an ideal product

product specification a precise description of the design, ingredients, processes and production methods, healthy and safety issues required to produce a food product

quality assurance the guarantee from the manufacturer that it has set up systems to ensure the production of a quality product

quality control the systems in place to monitor the quality of a product at certain stages during the production process. The steps taken by a manufacturer to ensure the product meets the requirements of the product specification

recipe engineering adapting an existing recipe for a different dietary group or target market group

Reference Nutrient Intake (RNI) the amount of a nutrient required by people in a particular dietary group

saturated fats that generally come from animal sources, for example, lard and suet

scaling up modifying a recipe so that it is suitable for large-scale production

secondary processing the conversion of primary processed food into food products, for example, turning flour into bread

sensory characteristics for example, appearance, colour, texture taste and aroma

sensory descriptors words used to describe the characteristics of a food product, for example, words like 'fishy', 'tasty', 'crunchy' and so on

shelf life the length of time a product can be stored before it becomes unsafe to eat or deteriorates

standard components ingredients that are ready prepared and processed, used by manufacturers to make more complex food

star diagram a diagrammatic method of showing the profile of a food product

sterilization a heat treatment used to remove all micro-organisms

system the series of tasks needed to create a finished product. Systems are made up of inputs, processes and outputs

target market group those customers identified as having needs or wants that the food manufacturer can fulfil with new or existing products. The target market group will have certain unique and identifiable characteristics

tolerances the amount of flexibility allowed in specified limits or targets for things like oven temperature, product weight, size and so on

toxins poisons harmful to humans produced by some micro-organisms

trans fats produced when food manufacturers pump hydrogen into oil

UHT ultra heat treatment – a form of sterilization

unsaturated fats mainly found in vegetable sources

Index